# THE
## Dying LAMENTATION and ADVICE
### OF
# Philip Kennifon,

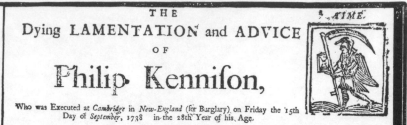

Who was Executed at *Cambridge* in *New-England* (for Burglary) on Friday the 15th
Day of *September*, 1738 in the 28th Year of his Age.

*All written with his own Hand, a few Days before his Death:*

And publifhed at his earneft Defire, for the good of Survivors.

GOod People all both great & fmall,
  to whom thefe Lines fhall come,
A warning take by my fad Fall,
  and unto God return.

You fee me here in Iron Chains,
  In Prifon now confin'd,
Within twelve Days my Life muft end.
  my Breath I muft refign.

For Sin hath fo inclofed me,
  and compafs'd me about,
That I am now remedilefs,
  if Mercy help not out.

O let me then this Caution give
  to every one of you,
Especially to you that live
  in Sin and fpend your Youth.

To feek the Lord with one accord,
  now while you have the Light,
Left you be left, and then you'l fall
  In darkfom gloomy Night.

O then the Judgments of the Lord
  will on you faft abide;
And then your Pleafures all will flee,
  and all your Friends likewife.

For this I fee apparently,
  and by Experience know,
For now my Friends do from me flee
  and laugh to fee my Wo.

None of my Friends have I to fee,
  nor none to comfort me;
For I am left of God to fee
  my doleful Mifery.

Now I muft go my Doom to hear.
  my Wages to receive;
O how fhall I endure to hear?
  O it doth make me grive.

For when my Sins are judg'd and try'd,
  the Heavens will record
That God is juft, all muft abide
  the Judgment of the Lord.

He doth prepare his mortal Dart,
  his Arrows keen and fharp;
For them that do him perfecute,
  and do at Mifchief laugh.

He doth rebuke the Heathen kind,
  and wicked to confound;
That afterwards the Memory
  of them cannot be found.

Thus I am made a Laughing Stock,
  to all that's round about;
My Enemies do at me mock,
  they clip their Hands and fhout.

O let me be a Warning then
  to every one of you;
That fee me here confin'd in Chains,
  left you with me fhould rue.

Alas, I am as brought to Grave,
  and almoft turn'd to Duft;
My Portion here you fee I have
  with rude Men and unjuft.

Fear and the Snare is come on me,
  Wafte and Deftruction;
Because that I refuf'd to hear
  the Lord's Inftruction.

My Heart doth pant for want of Breath
  it panteth in my Breaft;
With Terror, and the dread of Death
  my Soul is much oppreft.

Such dreadful Fears on me do fall,
  that I therewith do quake;
Such Sorrow overwhelmeth me,
  that I no Shift can make.

My wicked Life fo far excels,
  that I fhall fet therein;
But Lord forgive my great mifdeeds,
  and purge from my Sin.

So come I to the Throne of Grace,
  where Mercy doth abound;
Defiring Mercy for my Sins,
  to heal my deadly Wounds.

*Cautions and Warnings.*

MY dearest Friends, before I die,
  these Verfes I have made;
Commit them to your Memory,
  mind them when I am dead.

First unto God do bequeath
  my wicked finful Soul,
To be with Chrift in final Reft,
  where nothing can controul.

Next unto you thefe Lines I write
  to caution you to fear
The Lord of Heaven and of Might,
  and love your Saviour dear.

O that my Eyes with Tears of Blood
  as Waters down might flow;
So that my Writing might do good,
  which to the World I fhow.

O that you would this Warning take
  by my unhappy Fall;
So as that you may then efcape
  the endlefs burning Thraul.

Do not your felf with that content,
  not any fuch ill kind;
To fay at laft if I repent
  then Mercy I fhall find.

That is a very foolifh Thing,
  for you for to believe;
The Devil doth but tempt to Sin,
  at laft he'l you deceive.

That is his whofe Employment then,
  in Scripture you may fee;

For to deceive the Sons of Men,
  and that we often fee.

If he be fuch an one as that,
  great Care we ought to take;
Left we fall in an evil Net,
  and cry when it's too late.

Remember *Efau* how he cry'd,
  when it was all too late;
And for the Bleffing he did cry,
  and earneftly did feek.

But all in vain, it was too late,
  his Time and Glafs was run;
Although he fought with Tears at laft,
  but it could not be found.

Remember well the wicked *Jews*,
  in Blindnefs they do live;
Becaufe they did their King refufe,
  and did not him believe.

O take ye heed the time,
  to fleep your Time away;
Who did our Saviour Chrift refufe,
  and fell into decay.

Fear ye the Lord, obey the King,
  live quietly together;
And ftrive for to be born again,
  that you may live for ever.

Fear to offend Almighty God,
  keep his Commandements;
Or he will fmite with his fore Rod,
  if you do not repent.

Let Heaven be your chiefeft Care,
  mind not this Earthly Mould;
But always ftrive to get a Share
  in your Redeemer's Fold.

For when you die, you will receive
  moft joyfully that Word,
*Enter thou in into my Reft,*
  there will you fee the Lord.

But if that you will obey
  the Call of God then,
He'l you cut off in midft of Days,
  your Glafs will foon be run.

Whilft Fools do hafte their Time to
  fpending in Sport the Day; (wafte,
Whilft that they jeft, let thy Heart reft
  in feeking Wifdom's Way.

Remember Death and Judgment too,
  mark what I here do fay,
Remember what I fay to you,
  think on the Judgment Day.

My Friends I die,

PHILLIP KENNISON.

*FINIS.*

Bofton, Printed and fold at the Heart and Crown in Cornhill; where may be had a Narrative of his Life, written by his own Ha

*loysius*

THE ALBERT A. BIEBER COLLECTION OF

# AMERICAN PLAYS, POETRY AND SONGSTERS

## A MOST UNUSUAL GATHERING OF EARLY AND MODERN AMERICAN LITERATURE, COVERING A VARIETY OF THEMES, *viz.:*

COLONIAL AMERICA—AMERICAN REVOLUTION—WAR OF 1812
SLAVERY AND THE CIVIL WAR—ABRAHAM LINCOLN
NEW YORK, NEW JERSEY, MASSACHUSETTS, PENNSYLVANIA
CALIFORNIA AND THE WEST 'AND SOUTH—INDIANS
—POLITICS—MASONIC SONGS—RARE IMPRINTS, ETC.

ILLUSTRATED WITH FACSIMILES
BIBLIOGRAPHICALLY DESCRIBED AND CATALOGUED
WITH ORIGINAL NOTES BY THE OWNER

COOPER SQUARE PUBLISHERS, INC.
New York
1963

Library of Congress Catalog Card No. 63-20133
Published by Cooper Square Publishers, Inc.
59 Fourth Avenue, New York 3, N. Y.
Printed in the United States of America

# AMERICAN VERSE AND WHAT IT SHOULD
## BE VALUED FOR

American Poetry is valuable not so much for the *quality* of its verse (which is, by the way, quite as good, averaging poet for poet, as is the verse of other countries), as it is for its richness in national and local themes and color, and especially as depicting the contemporary manners, customs, moral life and thought of that particular locality in which it is written. It is, in fact, an important link between the present and past generations, and from it we can derive an inside knowledge of Americans of those past generations—their ways and thoughts. The regular American histories serve their purpose for purely historical facts from a National standpoint; but Poetry, Plays, Songs, Ballads and Hymns give us an intimate view of the thoughts of the people themselves as well as being tinged with their own localisms.

Of course, we have our "High-Brow" poets, who treat verse from a lofty and spiritual standpoint, but it is the "Low-Brow" poets who, as a rule, record the history of the people in a way and manner that they (the people) best understand. Local Verse is always interesting if looked at from the standpoint mentioned, even though it is written in what our Professors of Literature call a "Doggerel" vein, but they have overlooked the fact that, as a rule, the writer was addressing a local audience in a local manner which the hearers or readers would readily understand. This is the type of poetry—the "Low-Brow," the Verses, Ballads and Songs of the People—of which we like to speak, which we record, and of which the present collection largely consists.

To conclude, we will repeat Mr. McKee's advice to collectors; he said:—"American collectors cannot afford to ignore two species of books, American History and American Literature. Those who do, are likely to regret it when it is too late; for not only do they possess the highest interest, but the day is coming when they will be sought for with the same avidity that Early English Literature is now." (From the Preface to the Thomas Jefferson McKee Catalogue of American Literature and Plays, 1900.) His words are coming true with every collection of this type that has been offered lately.

With best wishes to the successful bidders, I am,

Sincerely yours,

ALBERT A. BIEBER
Manasquan, New Jersey

# AMERICAN PLAYS

1. ADAMS (CHARLES F.). Rob, The Hermit; or, The Black Chapel of Maryland. A Romantic Drama. In Four Acts, dramatized from J. P. Kennedy's novel of "Rob of the Bowl." 12mo, original wrappers, pp. 34 and [2].
New York: Harold Roorback, Publisher [1879]

This was played at White's Opera House, Concord, N. H. Not in Sturges, McKee, Harris, Maier or New York Public Library collections.

2. ADAMS (SAMUEL HOPKINS). "Excess Baggage." [Photo Play.] Written on 42 large 8vo leaves.
ORIGINAL MANUSCRIPT.

3. [ALLINGHAM (JOHN TILL).] Lenfestey's Edition. 'Tis All a Farce, in Two Acts. As performed at the Philadelphia Theatre. 18mo, sewed, pp. 30 and advertisement leaf.
Philadelphia: Published by R. H. Lenfestey, No. 53, North Sixth Street, 1834

RARE. Not in Sturges, McKee, Harris or Maier collections. The only copy located is that in the New York Public Library list.

4. BAILEY (JOHN J.). Waldimar. A Tragedy, in Five Acts. (Not published.) 8vo, original cloth, pp. 124, [3], and 2 to 6.
New York, 1834

PRIVATELY PRINTED, PRESENTATION COPY to Mrs. Ellet, the poetess, from the author. Prologue written by Robt. C. Sands. Epilogue by Theodore S. Fay. Performed in New York and Philadelphia by Charles Kean, the noted actor. Dedicated to Lewis Cass.
Not in Sturges, Harris or Maier.

5. [BAKER (DELPHINE P.).] Solon, or, The Rebellion of '61. A Domestic and Political Tragedy by Delphine. "Truth Stranger than Fiction" . . . 8vo, original printed wrappers, pp. 74.
Chicago, Ill.: S. P. Rounds, Book and Job Printer, 46 State Street, 1862

A RARE CIVIL WAR PLAY in Prose form, verse interspersed throughout. With this item goes the separately printed Table of Characters, among which is Jefferson Davis, "Father of Solon" (the South), Abraham Lincoln, "Father of Nora" (the North), etc. Scenes: Washington and Missouri.
Not in Sturges, Roden, McKee, Maier, New York Public Library, Harris, etc.

6. [BAKER (G. M.).] Bonbons. A Musical and Dramatic Entertainment. 12mo, illustrated original printed wrappers, pp. [3], 140 to 189, [1].
Boston: Lee & Shepard . . . [1870]

Not in Roden, Sturges, McKee, Harris, Maier or New York Public Library List.

7. BANGS (JOHN KENDRICK). Katharine. A Travesty. 12mo, original printed wrappers, pp. 127 and [1]. [New York] MDCCCLXXXVIII (1888) PRIVATELY PRINTED. Author's third book. Not in Sturges or McKee.

### RARE PLAY BY NATHANIEL H. BANNISTER

8. BANNISTER (NATHANIEL H.). Gaulantus, A Tragedy in Five Acts. By Nathaniel H. Bannister, Author of "Caius Silius," "Marriage Contract," etc., etc. 16mo, sewed, pp. 67, title and some pages stained.
Cincinnati: Published by Flash, Ryder and Co. D. Murphy, Printer, 1836
EXTREMELY RARE PLAY. *Roden*, page 13; not in Sturges, McKee, Harris or New York Public Library catalogues. Roden gives collations of 4 titles and mentions 2 others by Bannister; Harris Catalogue lists one title; New York Public Library none, Sturgis none, etc., and yet this author wrote at least 50 plays—this will give an idea of the rarity of early plays by Bannister.

9. BARKER (JAMES N.). The Indian Princess; or, La Belle Sauvage. An Operatic Melo-Drame, in three acts. Performed at the Theatres Philadelphia and Baltimore. First acted April 6, 1808. 18mo, pp. [2] and 74.
Philadelphia: T. & G. Palmer, 1808
This copy besides its regular Philadelphia title, contains also the New York title-page, as issued. Based on an extract from Capt. Smith's *History of Virginia*, London, 1624.

10. BARKER (JAMES N.). Lopez and Wemyss' Edition. The American Acting Theatre. Marmion; or, The Battle of Flodden Field. A Drama, in five acts. By James N. Barker, Esq. with a portrait of Mrs. Duff, in the character of Marmion . . . 16mo, unbound, pp. 62.
Philadelphia: Published by A. R. Poole . . . [1826]
VERY RARE, far more so than the New York 1816 edition. Not in Sturges, McKee, Harris, etc. The portrait is missing, AS USUAL. A copy with the portrait would be an unusual sight.

11. BARKER (JAMES N.). Lopez and Wemyss' Edition. The American Acting Theatre. The Tragedy of Superstition, by James N. Barker, Esq. Author of Marmion, a Tragedy, and with a portrait of Mrs. Duff, in the character of Mary. The Plays carefully corrected from the Prompt books of the Philadelphia Theatre, By M. Lopez, Prompter. 16mo, unbound, pp. 68, few leaves ripped and last leaf slightly imperfect.
[Philadelphia.] Published by A. R. Poole, Chestnut Street, for the Proprietors [1826]
VERY RARE, not in Sturges or McKee collections. The portrait is missing, AS USUAL. A copy containing same would be an unusual sight.

12 BATEMAN (MRS. SIDNEY F.). Self; A Comedy, in three acts. 12mo, original printed wrappers, pp. 46 and [2].
New York: Samuel French, 121 Nassau Street [1856]
*Roden*, page 14. Not in Sturges, McKee, Harris, Maier, etc.

13 BERNARD (BAYLE). The Farmer's Story! A Domestic Drama, in Three Acts. *Etched frontispiece*. 18mo, original wrappers, pp. 48.
London: Thomas Hailes Lacy, Wellington Street, Strand [1836?]
The author was born in Boston, Mass. 1808; he wrote plays for a great many American actors, including Hackett, Yankee Hill, etc.
Not in Sturges, McKee, Harris or Roden. FINE COPY. No. 124 (in ink) of the New British Theatre (late Duncombe's).

2

14. BERNARD (BAYLE). The Minor Drama. No. I. The Irish Attorney: or, Galway Practice in 1770. A Farce in two acts . . . *Frontispiece*. 16mo, original printed wrappers, pp. 38.
New York: Berford & Co. No. 2 Astor House, and Taylor and Co., Baltimore, 1847

> RARE EDITION, no copy of this edition in Roden, Sturges, McKee, Harris, Maier, New York Public Library, etc.

15. BERNARD (BAYLE). The Irish Attorney; or, Galway Practice in 1770. A Farce in Two Acts . . . 16mo, original wrappers, pp. 38.
New York: William Taylor & Co. [1847]

> This edition has alterations and additions by Powers, the noted actor who played the part of the hero, Pierce O'Hara. Not in Roden, Sturges, McKee, Harris, Maier or New York Public Library collections.

16. BERNARD (BAYLE). The Middy Ashore. A Farce, in One Act . . . *Etched frontispiece*. 18mo, original wrappers, pp. 24.
London: Thomas Hailes Lacy, Wellington Street, Strand [1836?]

> See note to his *Farmer's Story*. Not in Sturges or McKee. Roden mentions this title but gives no collation, he lists but two American reprint titles by Bernard. FINE COPY. No. 177 (in ink) of The New British Theatre (late Duncombe's).

17. BOUCICAULT (DION). Alma Mater: or, A Cure for Coquettes. An Original Comedy, in Three Acts . . . as performed at the Theatre Royal Haymarket. 12mo, original printed wrappers, pp. 48.
London: Webster & Co. . . . [1842]

> With an interesting preface to Webster, the publisher and fellow-author, by Dion Boucicault. Webster Schilling edition. Not in Sturges, Harris, McKee or Maier collections.

18. BOUCICAULT (DION). The Colleen Bawn; or, the Brides of Garryowen. A Domestic Drama, in Three Acts . . . 12mo, wrappers, pp. 42.
Printed but not Published [New York, 1860]

> THE VERY SCARCE PRIVATELY PRINTED ISSUE. This edition not known to Roden, and lacking in the Sturges, McKee, Harris and Maier collections.

19. BOUCICAULT (DION). A Drawing-room in the Admiral De Brevan's [etc.] characters, Paul-Dominique; Seraphine, Dr. Sechard, etc. Tall 8vo, original plain wrappers, sewed, pp. 38. [New York] *circa* 186–?

> The above privately issued play, evidently sent out by Boucicault for critical circulation, was issued without title-page, and has written on first page: *Return to Dion Boucicault, 20 E. 15th S. N. Y.*, in the author's handwriting. THE RAREST OF BOUCICAULT'S PLAYS and not known or listed in any catalogue of American Verse or Plays.

20. BOUCICAULT (DION). A Lover by Proxy. A Comedietta in One Act . . . as performed at the Theatre Royal Haymarket. 12mo, original printed wrappers, pp. 28. London: Webster & Co. [1842?]

> Regular edition issued without plate. Price 6d. Not in Sturges, McKee, Harris or Maier collections.

21. BOUCICAULT (DION). The Octoroon; or, Life in Louisiana. A Play in five acts . . . 18mo, original wrappers, pp. 40 and [1]. [Boston: 1876]

> Printed, Not Published. VERY SCARCE. All copies located lack the extra leaf at end containing Lee and Shepard's list of books with 1876 date. Not in Sturges, McKee or Maier.

22. BOUCICAULT (DION). Old Heads and Young Hearts. A Comedy in five acts . . . as performed at the Theatre Royal Haymarket. . . . *Illustrated with an engraving, by Mr. Brewer*, taken during the representation of the piece. 12mo, original printed wrappers, pp. 63.

London: Published at the National Acting Drama Office . . . [1844]

Not in Sturges, Harris, McKee, Maier, etc. This is the copyrighted edition issued with an engraving, Price 1s. Only those with this National Acting Drama Office imprint were issued with plates. The Webster Co. Shilling edition was issued without plates.

23. BROUGHAM (JOHN). Life in New York; or, Tom and Jerry on a Visit. A Comic Drama, in two acts . . . 16mo, original printed wrappers, pp. 26 and [2]. New York: Samuel French, 1856

French's American Drama, No. 94. ORIGINAL ISSUE. Not in Sturges or McKee.

24. BROUGHAM (JOHN). Metamora; or the Last of the Pollywoogs. A Burlesque in two acts. 16mo, original printed wrappers, pp. 18.

Boston: H. W. Swett . . . [1857?]

SCARCE EDITION. Not in Sturges, McKee or Maier.

25. BUCHANAN (THOMPSON). Life. A Photo Play. Large 8vo, 30 leaves, wrappers. No place, no date

Original typewritten manuscript. Scene begins at Yale College, works along to Sing Sing Prison, New York, etc.

## FIRST REVOLUTIONARY WAR PLAY PRESENTED IN NEW YORK

26. BURK (JOHN). Bunker-Hill; or, the Death of General Warren; an Historic Tragedy, in Five Acts. By John Burk, late of Trinity College, Dublin. As played at the Theatres in America, for fourteen nights, with unbounded applause. Copy Right secured according to Law. 12mo, sewed, pp. 55, UNCUT EDGES. [New York: T. Greenleaf, 1797]

Letter of dedication to Aaron Burr by the author.

AN EXCESSIVELY RARE AMERICAN PLAY. Not in Wegelin, Sturges, Harris, McKee, Maier or New York Public Library catalogues. The imprint is lacking from this copy, but its rarity makes it desirable in spite of this slight defect which is remediable by any restorer.

"The first of the purely Revolutionary plays presented in New York was probably Bunker Hill or the Death of General Warren. It was played at the John Street Theatre in 1797; and it was followed next year by William Dunlap's Andre, at the Park Theatre."—Hutton's *Curiosities of the American Stage.*

27. [BURNETT (J. G.).] Blanche of Brandywine. An American Patriotic Spectacle. Dramatized for, and originally performed at Laura Keene's Theatre, Thursday, April 22, 1858, with unbounded success . . . 16mo, original wrappers, pp. 40. New York: Samuel French [1858]

*Roden*, page 28. A dramatization of George Lippard's romance by above name. Not in Sturges, McKee or Maier collections.

## THE FAIR AMERICANS, BY MRS. CARR, A PLAY OF THE WAR OF 1812

28. CARR (MRS.). The Fair Americans, An Original Comedy in Five Acts. By Mrs. Carr. To candour, taste, and justice, is consign'd, This trembling offspring of a feeble mind. 16mo, pp. 4 and 44.

*[Continued*

[ No. 28. CARR (MRS.)—*Continued* ]

Philadelphia: Printed and published by Mrs. Carr, No. 5 Hartung's Alley, and may be had at Mrs. Neale's Library, No. 201, Chestnut-street, and at Mrs. Phillip's Library, No. 119 South Third-street: 1815

AN EXTREMELY RARE PLAY, written, printed and published by the authoress and sold by her lady friend booksellers. Lacking in the Sturges, McKee, Harris, NewYork Public Library and other collections consulted. Name and writing on title and few lines of text gone from Prologue leaf. Desirable even though slightly imperfect, as to DUPLICATE IT WOULD BE A PROBLEM.

29. CARTER (JOHN H.). The Log of Commodore Rollingpin: His Adventures Afloat and Ashore. *With Numerous Comic Illustrations.* 8vo, cloth, pp. 258 and [6].

New York: G. W. Carleton & Co., Publishers . . . MDCCCLXXIV

Contains in Part II: Mississippi Ballads and a Drama in four Acts, entitled: "The Blood-stained Boot-Jack; or, the Chamber-maid's Revenge." Also contains a chapter entitled: "Bret Harte in St. Louis, 1873."
Not in Johnson, Roden, Sturges, McKee, Maier, Harris or New York Public Library collections.

30. CHRISTY (E. BYRON). Box and Cox. In One Act. Africanized expressly for George Christy. With the Stage Business, Cast of Characters, Relative Positions, etc. 16mo, original printed wrappers, pp. [3] and 8 to 21.

New York: Happy Hours Company . . . [1870?]

Not in Sturges, Harris, McKee, etc.

31. [COBB (JAMES).] The Cherokee, An Opera, in Three Acts, as performed at the Theatre-Royal, Drury-Lane. By the Author of the Haunted Tower. 16mo, new cloth, pp. 47 and [1].

London: Printed in the Year M.DCC.XCV. Price Six-Pence

FIRST EDITION. Not in Sturges, McKee, Harris, New York Public Library or Maier. Scene is laid in a forest in America, the Indians are Malooko, Zamorin, Ontayo, Patowmac. Sonneck, *Opera Librettos before 1800* (page 276, Volume One). Title and several pages have bottom margins repaired. CLEAN COPY.

32. COLLINS (JOHN A.). The Anti-Slavery Picknick: A Collection of Speeches, Poems, Dialogues, and Songs; intended for use in Schools and Anti-Slavery Meetings. 12mo, unbound, pp. 144.

Boston: H. W. Williams . . . MDCCCXLII

Contains the following plays:—"Instincts of Childhood," in 2 parts, by John Neal; "Mysterious Artist," 3 scenes; "Duty and Safety of Emancipation," one scene. Not in Sturges, McKee, Harris or Maier collections.

33. COLMAN (GEORGE, THE YOUNGER). Inkle and Yarico: An Opera, in Three Acts. As performed at the Theatre-Royal in the Hay-Market, On Saturday, August 11th, 1787. 8vo, boards, loose, pp. 75.

London: Printed for G. G. J. and J. Robinson, Pater-Noster-Row [1787]

The scene of above play was laid on the "American Main," later in Barbados.

34. CONRAD (ROBERT T.). Alymere, or The Bondman of Kent [play]; and Other Poems. 8vo, original cloth, pp. 329, [6 of Advertisements].

Philadelphia: E. H. Butler & Co., 1852

The play takes up to page 165; Poem, "On the Death of General Taylor," (5pp.) etc. Conrad was distinguished as an Orator and Dramatic writer. Not in Sturges, Maier or New York Public Library.

35. [CRAFTS (WILLIAM).] The Sea-Serpent; or, Gloucester Hoax. A Dramatic Jeu d'Esprit, in three acts. Ecce aliud miraculum!—Livy. Copy-Right secured according to Law. 12mo, sewed, UNCUT, pp. 34.
Charleston [South Carolina]: Printed and Published by A. E. Miller, No. 101, Queen street . . . 1819

> The author of above play was born in Charleston, S. C., Jan. 24, 1787, graduated at Harvard, 1805; became an eminent lawyer in his native city, and was for some time editor of the Charleston [S. C.] *Courier*. A VERY RARE SOUTHERN PLAY, not in Sturges, Harris, Maier or New York Public Library catalogues.
> The word "Sea-Serpent" and letter "X" of Hoax are missing and supplied by a former owner in ink. This is an uncut copy and can be made into a fine copy by any skilful restorer.

36. CUSHING (C. C. S.). Nathan Hale of '73. A Drama in Four Acts. *Illustrated.* Narrow 8vo, wrappers, pp. [12] and 88.
New Haven, Connecticut: Yale Publishing Association, MCMVII

> No. 231 of 500 copies printed. Autograph on wrapper of Stuart Phelps Dodge, Public Ledger, Aiken, South Carolina. Play on the "Martyr" Spy of the American Revolution. Not in Sturges.

37. DAVID AND URIAH. A Drama, in five acts: founded on the exploits of the man after God's own heart . . . 12mo, pp. 34 and [2].
Philadelphia: Published by the Author. 1835

> Not in Sturges, McKee or New York Public Library List. The copy noted by Roden in his bibliography of *Later American Plays* lacked the 2 extra pages of the Epilogue.

38. DUNLAP (WILLIAM). Abaellino, The Great Bandit. A Grand Dramatic Romance in five acts. Translated from the German and adapted to the New York Theatre. By William Dunlap, Esq. Third edition—copyright secured. 16mo, unbound, uncut edges, pp. 60.
New York: Published by D. Longworth, at the Dramatic Repository, Shakespeare-Gallery. Jan., 1814

> CHOICE UNCUT COPY of this third edition. Not in Sturges, McKee, Harris, etc. Wegelin in his *Dunlap Bibliography* mentions this edition but gives no collation.

### UNKNOWN PLAY BY WILLIAM DUNLAP

39. [DUNLAP (WILLIAM).] Chains of the Heart; or, The Slave by Choice, in Three Acts. By Prince Hoare. As Performed at the New York Theatre, from the Prompt-Book. By permission of the Manager. 32mo, unbound, pp. 96.
New-York: Printed and Published by D. Longworth, at the Dramatic Repository, Shakespeare-Gallery, 1804

> Under the Dramatis Personae page is the following printed note, viz: "The passages marked with inverted commas, are omitted in the performance, *and those in italic, are added by William Dunlap, esq.*"
> NOT IN WEGELIN'S *Dunlap Bibliography*, LACKING IN THE McKEE, HARRIS, STURGES AND ALL OTHER NOTABLE COLLECTIONS OF AMERICAN POETRY AND PLAYS.

### UNKNOWN ISSUE OF DUNLAP'S PLAY "LEICESTER"

40. [DUNLAP (WILLIAM).] Leicester. | A Tragedy. | Vol. I signature H. | 12mo, pp. [5] and 90 to 150. [New York, 1806?]

> The collation of the above play is identical with the 1807 edition described in Wegelin's *Dunlap Bibliography*, but OF THIS ISSUE I FIND NO RECORD.
> [*Continued*

Dunlap's page "To the Reader" in this play states,—"The following poem, my first effort in tragic composition, and the first American Tragedy produced upon the stage, was written in the year 1790, and first played, at New York in 1794. Its success confirmed my attachment to the drama. . . May, 1806. W. Dunlap." Not in Sturges, McKee, etc.

41.  DUNLAP (WILLIAM).  Peter the Great; or, the Russian Mother: A Play in Five Acts.  Altered from the German by William Dunlap.  As performed at the New York Theatre.  16mo, sewed, pp. [5] and 6 to 56.

New York: Published by David Longworth, at the Dramatic Repository, Shakespeare Gallery, March, 1814

## UNKNOWN ADDITION TO DUNLAP'S "YANKEE CHRONOLOGY"

42.  [DUNLAP (WILLIAM).]  The Renegade; A Grand Historical Drama, in three acts interspersed with music.  Founded on Dryden's Don Sebastian, King of Portugal.  By Frederick Reynolds.  16mo, unbound, pp. 54 and 2.

New York: Published by D. Longworth . . . Feb., 1813

Not in Wegelin's *Dunlap Bibliography*, Sturges, McKee, Harris, etc., etc.
The Dunlap interest lies in the last leaf, entitled, "YANKEE NAVAL CHRONOLOGY; BEING A CONTINUATION OF YANKEE CHRONOLOGY BY WILLIAM DUNLAP, ESQ. . ." On verso of this page is an almost full-page woodcut of Decatur's *Victory* (with text:) Superfine Decatur Playing Cards, sold, wholesale and retail at 11 Park near the Theatre (etc.).  Slightly stained and ripped.

43.  [DUNLAP (WILLIAM).]  The Shipwreck; A Comic Opera, in two acts.  By Samuel James Arnold as performed at the Theatre New-York and Drury-Lane.  From the New-York Prompt Book, By permission of the Manager. 18mo, pp. 43, [one blank] and 4 of Advertisements.

New-York: Published by D. Longworth, at the Dramatic Repository, Shakespeare-Gallery.  1805

With alterations and additions by the Manager of the New York Theatre, *i. e.*, William Dunlap.
EXTREMELY RARE DUNLAP ITEM, not in Wegelin's *Dunlap Bibliography*.  Not in Sturges, McKee, Harris and other noted collections.  Autograph of Sylvester Simmons Southworth on title and blank page at end.  Word "Shipwrecked" on title and some other words throughout blocked out in green crayon.

44.  DUNLAP (WILLIAM).  The Wife of Two Husbands; A Drama, in five acts, interspersed with Songs, Choruses, Music and Dances.  By W. Dunlap, Esq.  As performed at the New-York Theatre.  (Copy-right secured.) 16mo, unbound, pp. 55.

New York.  Published by D. Longworth, at the Dramatic Repository, Shakespeare Gallery, Feb., 1811 (second edition)

THIS SECOND EDITION IS RARE.

45.  DUNLAP (WILLIAM).  Yankee Chronology; or, Huzza for the Constitution! A Musical Interlude, in one Act.  To which are added, The Patriotic Songs of The Freedom of the Seas, and Yankee Tars.  By W. Dunlap, Esq. 16mo, sewed, pp. 16.

New York: Published by D. Longworth, at the Dramatic Repository, . . . Dec., 1812

Not in Sturges.  Wegelin's *Dunlap Bibliography* calls for 18 pp., which is a mistake as this item is absolutely perfect in 16 pages, as was also the McKee copy of 16 pages.  FINE COPY.

46. DURIVAGE [O. E.]. Olivine's New York Theatre, No. IX. The Lady of the Lions. A Burlesque in one act. By Mr. Durivage, Comedian. Edited by Wayne Olivine Comedian, Manager of the Troy Museum, and late Manager of the Chestnut Street Theatre, Philadelphia, Varieties, Washington, D. C. etc., etc. 12mo, original printed wrappers, pp. 20.
New York: Published for the Proprietor, by O. A. Roorbach, Jr. . . .
no date

Cast of players given for 1856 at the Holiday St. Theatre Balt.—St. Louis, Mo.—Bowery, N. Y.—Albany, N. Y. SCARCE. *Roden*, page 46. Not in Sturges, McKee, etc.

47. FITCH (CLYDE). Nathan Hale. A Play. In Four Acts. *Frontispiece and other illustrations.* 8vo, boards, uncut edges, pp. [10] and 100.
New York: R. H. Russell, MDCCCXCIX

FIRST EDITION. Not in Sturges, McKee or Maier collections.

48. FORREST (HARRY). Marie Antoinette: Queen of France. An Historical Drama, in five Acts, with a Prologue. From the Italian Tragedy written for Madame Ristori By Signor Giacometti. Adapted and arranged by Harry Forrest, New York, 1867. 12mo, sewed, pp. 72.
London: Thomas Hailes Lacy, 89 Strand, *circa* 1869

Unknown to Roden—not in Sturges, McKee, Harris, etc.

49. FOWLER (MANLEY B.). The Prophecy; or Love and Friendship. A Drama in three acts. 18mo, sewed, pp. 34.
New York: Murden and Thompson, July, 1821

Very scarce, not in Sturges collection. An author of whom very little appears to be known although he wrote several other plays.

50. FULLER (FRANCES A. AND METTA V.). Poems of Sentiment and Imagination with Dramatic and Descriptive Pieces. 8vo, original cloth, pp. 264, [8].
New York: A. S. Barnes & Co., Publishers, No. 51 John Street, 1851

The Dramatic piece is "Azlen," pp. 133 to 166 inclusive. Not in Roden, Sturges, McKee or Maier.

51. GENTLEMAN'S MAGAZINE: For July 1754. . . . By Sylvanus Urban. 8vo, original marbled boards, pp. [3], 300 to 342.
[L]ondon [*sic*] Printed by D. Henry and R. Cave [*sic*] at St. John's Gate [1754]

OF VERY EARLY AMERICAN DRAMATIC INTEREST containing:—A Song set to Music: Prologue and Epilogue at Philadelphia. On Monday the 15th of April a company of Comedians from London opened a New Theatre in Philadelphia; on which occasion the following Prologue and Epilogue were spoken by Mr. Rigby and Mrs. Hallam. With engraved bookplate of Colonel Talbot, Malahide Castle.

52. GLIEBE (FRANCIS DE SALES). The Planting of the Cross [in Santa Barbara, California]. A [Dramatic] Sketch, written for the Bicentenary of the birth of Junipero Serra, O. F. M., Founder of the California Missions, celebrated at Santa Barbara, November 24th, 1913. *Portrait.* 12mo, original wrappers, pp. 36.
[Morning Press Print, Santa Barbara, California, November, 1913]

SCARCE, PRIVATELY PRINTED PLAY.

53. GUSTAVUS VASA: A Tragedy in Five Acts, written by Henry Brooke, with Alterations and Amendments. As performed at the New Theatre in Boston. 16mo, unbound, pp. 62.

Boston: Printed for John West, No. 75, Cornhill, *circa* 1795

On account of the alterations and amendments this must be considered an American Adaptation. Not in Sturges, McKee, New York Public Library, etc.

54. HALE (NATHAN M.). A Dialogue, for Society Exhibitions, August, 1802 [in 2 Acts]; [ALSO] A Lampoon on the prevailing political and religious sentiments of the day, March [?] 1803 by S. D. Burbank. [A local poem on Braintree, Mass.] 2 vols. in one, 4to, sewed, pp. 31 for play, and 11 for poem of 411 lines. No place [1803]

CONTEMPORARY MANUSCRIPT, and as such its rarity is unquestioned.

55. HALL (A. OAKEY). A Coroner's Inquisition. A Farce in One Act . . . as performed at Burton's Theatre. 16mo, original wrappers, pp. 20.

New York: Samuel French [1857]

SCARCE. Hall was at one time Mayor of New York, he wrote plays, poems and tales. Not in Sturges.

56. [HALL (LOUISA J.—Mrs. E. B. Hall, of Providence, R. I.).] Miriam; A Dramatic Poem. By the Author of "Joanna of Naples." Second edition revised. 12mo, cloth, pp. 11 and 2 to 122.

Boston: H. P. Nichols and Company . . . 1838

SCARCE. Second edition, corrected. Not in Sturges.

57. HALL (LOUISA J.—Mrs. E. B. Hall, of Providence, R. I.). Miriam and Joanna of Naples, with Other Pieces in Verse and Prose. 8vo, original cloth, pp. [2], 6 to 403. Boston: Wm. Crosby and H. P. Nichols . . . 1850

In this edition the author's play "Miriam" has been revised, pp. 115 to 131 contain a "Dramatic Fragment." This edition not in *Roden*. Lacking in Sturges, McKee, and Maier collections.

58. HAMILTON (COSMO) AND ARNOLD (LAWRENCE). Marriage. (Alternative Title—"Man and Wife.") 4to, 2 and 47 leaves. No place, no date

ORIGINAL TYPEWRITTEN MANUSCRIPT PHOTOPLAY.

59. HARRISON (MRS. BURTON). Alice in Wonderland. A Play for Children in Three Acts. Dramatized by Mrs. Burton Harrison. With Tableaux, Songs, and Dances. *Illustrations by John Tenniel.* 8vo, unbound, pp. 35.

New York: The De Witt Publishing House[1890]

Not in Sturges, McKee, Maier or New York Public Library (which has the Chicago edition only), THE ONE ABOVE IS THE EARLIER EDITION. *Roden*, pp. 58, gives no collation, evidently has not seen a copy. Mrs. Harrison is the well-known Virginia novelist.

60. HARRISON (MRS. BURTON). A Russian Honeymoon, A Comedy in Three Acts. Adapted by Mrs. Burton Harrison From the French of Eugène Scribe. *Frontispiece.* 8vo, unbound, uncut, pp. 68.

New York: The Dewitt Publishing House. MDCCCXC (1890)

Not in Roden, Sturges, McKee, Maier or New York Public Library catalogues.

61. [HARWOOD (JOHN E.).] John Bull; or, the Englishman's Fire-Side: A Comedy in five acts. By George Colman the Younger. As performed at the Theatres New York and Philadelphia . . . *To which is added the Epilogue, as altered and spoken by Mr. Harwood, in the New York Theatre.* 18mo, pp. 86 and [2]. New York. Published by David Longworth, At the Dramatic Repository, Shakespeare Gallery. 1808

SECOND EDITION. RARE. Contains the Philadelphia and New York Cast. Epilogue and Birth, Christening and Marriage of Dennis Brulgruddery written and sung by Mr. Harwood. Harwood married Miss Bache, a granddaughter of Benjamin Franklin, he died in Germantown, Pa., 1809.

62. HOLLENIUS (L. J.). Maria and Magdalena. A Play, in Four Acts. Adapted for the American Stage from the German Original of Paul Lindau. . . . 16mo, original printed wrappers, pp. 44 and [4 of advertisements].
New York: Robert M. Dewitt [1874]

*Roden*, page 62. Not in Sturges, McKee, New York Public Library, etc.

63. HUNTINGTON (REV. GURDON). The Shadow Land, And Other Poems (including the Guests of Brazil). 8vo, original cloth, pp. 506, [2 of notes].
New York: James Miller . . . 1861

Not in Sturges, McKee or Maier. This edition not in *Roden*. "The Guests in Brazil, or The Martyrdom of Frederick" is a Tragedy. Among the other poems are: "Poetry and Romance of the Indian Country and its Tribes," "Washington at the Battle of Princeton," etc.

64. HUTTON (JOSEPH). The School for Prodigals: A Comedy, in five acts. By Joseph Hutton. As performed at the New Theatre, Philadelphia. 18mo, unbound, pp. 62.
New-York: Published by D. Longworth, at the Dramatic Repository, Shakespeare Gallery. 1809

Not in Sturges. The Prologue was spoken by Cone (Spencer H.) of Princeton, New Jersey, the only American-born Actor at that time playing on the American Stage. Cone later became a famous Baptist Minister of America.

65. HUTTON (JOSEPH). The Wounded Hussar, or, Rightful Heir: A Musical Afterpiece, in two acts. By Joseph Hutton. Author of the School for Prodigals. As performed at the New Theatre Philadelphia. 18mo, unbound, pp. 24. New-York: Published by D. Longworth. At the Dramatic Repository . . . 1809

THE RARE NEW YORK ISSUE. Not in the Sturges, McKee or Harris catalogues.

66. JOHNSON (JAMES C.). The May Festival. A Musical Recreation for Flower Time. 16mo, original printed wrappers, pp. 36.
Boston: Oliver Ditson & Co. [1844]

Not in Roden, Sturges, Harris, McKee, Maier, etc.

67. JOHNSON (WILLIAM). Benedict Arnold, The Traitor. By William Johnson. An Historical Drama, relating of the Treason of Benedict Arnold and his death. 12mo, original printed wrappers, pp. 47.
No place or printer, copyright 1891

PRIVATELY PRINTED, AND RARE. Not in Sturges, McKee, Maier or New York Public Library collections.

68. JOSAPHARE (LIONEL). Christopher. 16mo, cloth, pp. 73.
San Francisco: Privately Printed, 1921

PRIVATELY PRINTED PLAY BY A CALIFORNIA AUTHOR.

69. JUDAH (SAMUEL B. H.). Odofriede; The Outcast; A Dramatic Poem. 8vo, sheep back, marbled sides, pp. 89 and [6].
　　　　　New York: Wiley and Halsted, Wall-Street MDCCCXII (1822)
　　　　　FINE COPY. NOW VERY SCARCE.

70. [KELLY (THOMAS J. F.).] Henry IV. of Germany; A Tragedy in Five Acts. 8vo, original cloth, pp. 85.
　　　　　New York: Printed by Osborn & Buckingham . . . MDCCCXXXV (1835)
　　　　　*Roden* gives the date "1855" instead of "1835" (error?). Not in Sturges, McKee, Harris, Maier or New York Public Library.

71. KEMBLE (MISS FANNY). Francis the First: A Tragedy in Five Acts. ¡With other Poetical Pieces. Sixth American Edition in which is included An Original Memoir. And *A Full Length Portrait*. 8vo, original printed wrappers, pp.72.
　　　　　New York: Peabody & Co., Broadway, 1833
　　　　　THE FIRST COPYRIGHTED EDITION AND THE BEST. The finest Actress that ever played on the American Stage. The authoress became the wife of Pierce Butler of Philadelphia in 1834. Unfortunately they could not agree and Butler won the divorce suit in 1848; he died in Georgia, 1867.
　　　　　RARE. Not in Sturges, Roden, Maier or New York Public Library List.

72. LATHROP (GEORGE PARSONS). The Scarlet Letter. Dramatic Poem. Opera by Walter Damrosch. 8vo, original printed wrapper, pp. 40.
　　　　　[Boston: Privately printed, 1895]
　　　　　THIS IS THE FIRST EDITION. *Roden* lists the New York, 1896, edition. Not in Sturges, McKee, Maier or New York Public Library catalogues. Lathrop married Nathaniel Hawthorne's daughter.

73. LAZARUS (EMMA). Songs of a Semite: The Dance to Death [A Historical Tragedy in five Acts], and Other Poems. 8vo, original wrappers, pp. [9] and 6 to 80, [2]. 　New York: Office of "The American Hebrew" . . . 1882
　　　　　The Tragedy has its own title, in fact the "Songs of a Semite" title was added afterwards, the original title really being "The Dance to Death," etc. Not in Sturges McKee or Harris.

74. LELAND (OLIVER S.). Blue and Cherry. A Comedy, In One Act. 16mo, original printed wrappers, pp. 30.
　　　　　Boston: Charles H. Spencer, Agent, 1871
　　　　　Not in Roden, Sturges, McKee, New York Public Library, etc.

75. LEWIS (EDGAR). "His Masterpiece." Large 8vo, 14 leaves.
　　　　　[New York] no date
　　　　　ORIGINAL MANUSCRIPT of a Photo Play, originally purchased by some motion picture company for $25.00.

76. LOOKUP (ALEXANDER). Excelsior, or, The Heir Apparent. Showing the adventures of a promising and wealthy Young Man, and his devoted friends; and presently entwined with the varying story; The Key to a Diamond United States, or, A Vitally Consolidated Republic, A Perfect Union, Otherwise Kingdom of Heaven. Likewise giving, in picturesque dramatic dialogue, the notorious actions and secret lives of two celebrated Dictators of Party, and leaders in Political Convention the whole embodied in A Thrilling and Exquisite Poetical Romance. 8vo, unbound, pp. 108.
　　　　　New-York & London: Kennedy, Publisher, 483 Broadway, 1860
　　　　　Political play, not in Roden, Sturges, McKee, Harris, Maier or New York Public Library.

77. LOOKUP (ALEXANDER). The Granddaughter of the Caesars; or, the Hag of the Earth and Syren of the Waters: containing, besides, a Pathetic Story of Greed's Victims and Difficulty's Brokers [9 more lines of title]. 8vo, unbound, pp. 107.

New York & London: Kennedy, Publisher, 483 Broadway, 1860

A satiric play; scene begins in New York City. Not in Roden, Sturges, McKee, Harris, Maier or New York Public Library.

78. LOOKUP (ALEXANDER). The Soldier of The People; or, The World's Deliverer. 8vo, unbound, pp. 108.

New-York & London: Kennedy, Publisher, 483 Broadway, 1860

A political play, scene laid in Washington. Not in Roden, Sturges and beforementioned collections.

79. LOVER'S QUARRELS: or, Like Master, Like Man. A Farce,—in One Act, altered from "the Mistake." *Woodcut on title.* 32mo, unbound, pp. 20.

New York: Charles Wiley . . . 1825

Gives cast of players at Washington, Wemyss, Jefferson, Mrs. Anderson and Francis. NO OTHER COPY LOCATED.

80. MARRIOTT (CRITTENDEN). The Water Devil. By Crittenden Marriott, Author of "Miss Judith" (Vitagraph); Object, Matrimony, (Essanay).

[Washington, D. C., 1914]

ORIGINAL MANUSCRIPT, typewritten, 17 pages by this successful Photo Play writer.

81. MARRIOTT (MRS.). Chimera; or, Effusions of Fancy: A Farce in Two Acts. By Mrs. Marriott, of the Old American Company. 16mo, unbound, pp. 24. New-York: Printed by T. and J. Swords, No. 167 William Street, 1795

Lacking in Sturges, McKee, and other notable collections containing American Plays. Nice copy but unfortunately lacking 2 leaves. An opportunity to secure another copy of this play judging from its present and past rarity may mean an indefinitely long wait. Contains the cast of players among which are the Authoress and her husband. Autograph of *Andw. E. Rawen* on title.

82. MAURICE (MARK—[John Gore?]). The Manuscript; comprising The Fratricide, [Drama] and Miscellaneous Poems. By Mark Maurice. 16mo, new cloth, pp. 69, [1].

Boston: Printed by John H. Eastburn, 25, Congress Street, 1827

A RARE AMERICAN PLAY, not listed in Sturges, McKee, Harris, Maier or New York Public Library catalogues.

83. M'CREADY (WILLIAM). The Irishman in London or, the Happy African. A Farce in two Acts. As performed at the Philadelphia Theater. 16mo, new cloth, pp. 36.    Philadelphia, Published by Thomas H. Palmer, 1821

Gives the Philadelphia cast: Baker, Darley, Jefferson, etc. The author, an Irishman, came to America in 1826 and later periods until his career as a noted actor was ended by the Astor Theatre Riots in 1849.

84. MILLER (S. C.). The Men In Scarlet. [Photo] Drama. 2 folio leaves.

Perth Amboy, N. J. [1912]

ORIGINAL TYPEWRITTEN MANUSCRIPT. The author asked $35.00 for this play and received $15.00 from the Solax Co. Motion Picture Film, Manufacturers. Two letters refering to the sale are laid in.

85. MOORE (CHARLES LEONARD). Banquet of Palacios. A Comedy. 12mo, original cloth, pp. 196.
Philadelphia: C. L. Moore, 305 Walnut Street, 1889
AUTHOR'S EDITION AND THE FIRST. Not in Roden, Sturges, McKee or Maier.

86. MORTON (CHARLES H.). Women of the Day. An American Comedy of Modern Society in four Acts by Charles H. Morton, author of Poor and Proud, Our Country Cousins, If I were King [and 5 other titles], etc. etc. 12mo, original printed front wrapper.
Printed but not Published. Philadelphia, Pa. December, 1874
NOT IN RODEN. Another author like Bannister whose works are missing from the notable collections such as Sturges, McKee, Harris, New York Public Library, etc., and yet he was a prolific writer. This play was produced Dec. 14, 1874, in John Drew's Arch Street Theatre, Philadelphia. Authors name blind stamped on wrapper title.

87. MORTON (THOMAS). Columbus: or, A World Discovered. An Historica Play. As it is performed at the Theatre-Royal Covent-Garden. 8vo, new cloth, pp. [7], 2 to 66 and [2].
London: Printed for W. Miller, Old Bond-Street, 1792
FIRST EDITION. This play displays the customs of the Indians of Mexico and Peru. Not in Sturges, McKee, Harris or Maier.

88. MORTON (THOMAS). Columbus; or, A World Discovered; An Historical Play. As performed at the Theatre Royal, Covent Garden, and at the Philadelphia and Baltimore Theatres. 16mo, unbound, pp. 50 and [2].
Washington: Printed and Published by Davis & Force (Franklins Head) Pennsylvania Avenue, 1823
A VERY SCARCE EDITION, not in Sturges, etc. Contains Philadelphia cast.

89. NATURAL SON (THE): A Comedy in Five Acts. By Richard Cumberland, Esq. with alterations and amendments as performed at the Theatre in Boston. 16mo, unbound, pp. 54.
Boston: Printed for David West, No. 36, Marlborough-Street, and John West, No. 75, Cornhill, circa 1794
On account of the alterations and amendments this must be classed as an American Adaptation. Not in Sturges, McKee, New York Public Library, etc.

90. NEPHEW AS UNCLE (THE): A Comedy in three acts. From the French of Picard, through the German of Schiller. Played at Mr. Wm. S. Verplanck's, June 29, 1858. Translated for the Occasion. 12mo, original printed wrappers, pp. 33.
Newburgh, Gray & Lawson, Printers, 1858
PRIVATELY PRINTED. Not in Roden, Sturges, Harris, McKee, Maier or New York Public Library collections.

91. NEUMAN (HENRY). Self Immolation, or, The Sacrifice of Love. A Play— in three Acts. By Augustus Von Kotzebue. Faithfully translated from the German, By Henry Neuman, Esq. 12mo, unbound, pp. 57 and [3].
Boston: Printed for W. P. and L. Blake, at the Boston Book-Store, Cornhill, 1799
EXTREMELY RARE PLAY of which I find no copy in Sturges or elsewhere. This is an earlier translation than that of Smith which was a year later. The cast of players includes Hodgkinson, Turnbull, Powell, etc.

92. [NOAH (M. M.).] The Fortress of Sorrento: A petit Historical Drama in two acts. 16mo, unbound, pp. 28 and [4].
New York: Published by D. Longworth, at the Dramatic Repository, Shakespeare Gallery, 1808

Not in Sturges. The McKee copy lacked the four additional pages of Longworth's publications. Noah at the time he wrote this play was the great literary and political lion of New York City, later he was appointed Sheriff, and the only reason for turning him out of this office was "that the people thought it devilish hard that a Jew should hang a Christian!" "Pretty Christians, forsooth!" said the facetious Major Noah in his newspaper afterwards.

93. [NOAH (M. M.).] The Wandering Boys! or, The Castle of Olival! An Original Drama, in three acts. By John Kerr. *Plate.* 18mo, original wrappers, pp. 36.
London: Duncombe [183—]

SCARCE. Kerr adopted Noah's play as his own. Not in Sturges, Harris, McKee, Maier or New York Public Library catalogues.

94. OH! POOR OLD MAN SONGSTER, containing an unusually good selection of favorite songs and Ballads . . . It also contains an excellent Negro Sketch for three characters, entitled, "Oh, Poor Old Man," written as introductory to the capital song of that name; the music of which also appears in this book . . . 12mo, original colored wrappers, pp. 64.
New York: Robert M. De Witt . . . 1875

The Negro sketch takes up 8 pages with its song and music. UNCOMMON DE WITT SONGSTER AND ETHIOPIAN SKETCH. Not in Roden, Sturges, McKee, etc.

### RARE AND INTERESTING PROMPT COPY OF JOHN HOWARD PAYNE'S "BRUTUS"

95. PAYNE (JOHN HOWARD). Brutus; or, The Fall of Tarquin. An Historical Tragedy, in Five Acts. First represented at the Theatre Royal, Drury Lane, On Thursday Evening, December 3, 1818. Sixth Edition. 8vo, boards, pp. viii, [1], 2 to 56.
London: Printed by and for T. Rodwell, 5 Piccadilly . . . 1819

This interesting prompt book belonged to Vincent De Camp, early New York and Philadelphia actor (stage manager with I. I. Adams and Willard) of the Charleston (S. C.) Theatre. Then presented to Henry Willard, stage manager of the Charleston Theatre. Also has autograph of T. S. Cline, who played in the Chestnut Street Theatre, Philadelphia in 1835. And to make it still further interesting it has the autograph of C. R. Thorne, Chatham Theatre (New York) of which he was the manager. Thorne was also for a time manager of the Federal Street Theatre, Howard Athenaeum of Boston and Manager of the Union Theatre, Leavenworth, Kansas. Of the Chatham Street, New York Theatre, he was the first manager. He played at the Thelma Theatre, California, 1849, in the part of "Rolla."
The Payne play is MARKED THROUGHOUT WITH THE STAGE DIRECTIONS, making it an eye-picture of stage management of the period. Like all prompt books it shows much use. Bound in are 2 other plays,—"The Barber of Seville," Comic Opera, London, 1818 (prompt book), and Dibdin's "Melodrama Mad!" London, 1819.
Not in Sturges, Harris, McKee or Maier collections.

96. PAYNE (JOHN HOWARD). Charles the Second; or, The Merry Monarch: A Comedy in two acts, by John Howard Payne, Esq. Author of Brutus, The Lancers, Ali Pacha, Love in Humble Life, &c., Printed from the Acting copy, with remarks, biographical and critical by D—G. . . *Embellished with a fine engraving.* 18mo, original printed wrappers, pp. 45.
London: John Cumberland, 2 Cumberland Terrace, Camden New Town. [1832]

This edition not in Sturges or McKee. The above date is correct as verso of title advertises the *Ladies Penny Gazette* for 1832.

97. PAYNE (JOHN HOWARD). Brutus; or, The Fall of Tarquin. An Historical Tragedy, in five acts. First represented at The Theatre Royal, Drury-Lane. On Thursday Evening, Dec. 3, 1818. 16mo, sewed, UNCUT EDGES, PARTLY UNOPENED.
Baltimore: Printed and Published by J. Robinson. Circulating Library and Dramatic Repository, 1827

> RARE IN THIS CONDITION. This edition not in Sturges, McKee, Harris, etc. Speaking from experience, these later editions are far rarer than the first editions, as the rage for Payne had died down in the meantime, making the sale of later editions smaller. This is the play that revived the fortunes of the Drury Lane Theatre and of Kean the Actor.

98. PAYNE (JOHN HOWARD). Turner's Dramatic Library. Love in Humble Life. A Petite Comedy. In One Act . . . Correctly printed from the most approved acting copy . . . 18mo, original printed wrappers, pp. 27.
New York and Philadelphia: Turner and Fisher, no date

> VERY FINE COPY OF A SCARCE EDITION, not in Sturges, Wendell, McKee, Harris, New York Public Library, etc.

99. PAYNE (JOHN HOWARD). Sketch of the Life of John Howard Payne, as published in the Boston Evening Gazette compressed (with additions bringing it forward to a later period). By one of the editors of the New York Mirror: Now first printed in a separate form, with an appendix, containing selections of Poetry and further illustrations. 8vo, marbled wrappers, pp. [2] and 27.
Boston: Press of W. Warland Clap. 1833

> Written by Payne's friend Theodore S. Fay. The Appendix contains a few poems by Payne and "Scene from an Unpublished Play." The above pamphlet gives a full account of Payne's experiences with the London Managers, a curious chapter of literary history. Not in Sturges, McKee, Harris, Maier or New York Public Library catalogues. VERY RARE AND INTERESTING WORK.

100. PAYNE (JOHN HOWARD). Therese, The Orphan of Geneva: A Drama in Three Acts, Freely translated from the French and adapted to the English Stage. *Etched frontispiece.* 18mo, original printed wrappers, pp. 39.
London: Thomas Hailes Lacy, Wellington Street, Strand [183—]

> FINE COPY. No. 306 (in ink) of The New British Theatre (late Duncombe's). This edition not in Sturges, McKee, Harris, New York Public Library, etc.

101. PHILLIPS (HENRY ALBERT). A Daughter of the Tenements. 4to, 8 leaves and letter sheet extra.                                    [New York] 1917

> ORIGINAL TYPEWRITTEN MANUSCRIPT of a Photo Play. Enclosed is a letter referring to same and autographed by the author.

102. PHILLIPS (JONAS B.). Zamira, A Dramatic Sketch, and Other Poems. 12mo, original cloth, pp. 142, foxed.
New York: Printed by G. A. C. Van Beuren, 1835

> Not in McKee, Harris or Maier. VERY SCARCE.

103. PLOWDEN (MRS. F.). Virginia, An Opera, In Three Acts. The Overture and the whole of the Music New; The Melodies composed by the author of the Dialogue, and Harmonized by Dr. Arnold. 8vo, unbound, pp. [7], iv to viii, [1] and 2 to 63, [1].
London: Printed and Published by J. Barker, Dramatic Repository, Great Russell-Street, Covent-Garden, 1800

[*Continued*

    Historic play based on the arrival of Lord Delaware with 500 soldiers and large stores of provisions to succor the remnants of Sir Walter Raleigh's Colony. He also brought over an "Imperial Crown" and rich presents for Powhatan, who by the means of Manteo, a converted Indian who had been in England, was induced to befriend the English Settlement in Virginia.
    VERY RARE. Not in Swem's Bibliography of Virginia, Sturges, McKee, Harris, New York Public Library, etc.

104. QUAKER (THE). A Comic Opera, in two Acts as performed at the Philadelphia Theatre. 18mo, unbound, pp. 28.
New-York: Published by David Longworth, At the Dramatic-Repository, Shakespeare-Gallery, 1817
    RARE AMERICAN PLAY, not in Sturges and other noted collections.

105. [RICE (GEORGE E.).] An Old Play in a New Garb. Hamlet, Prince of Denmark. In three acts. *With 5 illustrations.* 12mo, original printed wrappers, pp. 59.       Boston, Ticknor, Reed, and Fields, MDCCCLII (1852)
    Roden does not mention the five illustrations in his collection. Not in Sturges Sale

106. RICE (K. McDOWELL). A Successful Stratagem. A Comedy in One Act. 12mo, original wrappers, pp. 30.     [Worthington, Mass., 1902]
    Uncommon American Play, PRIVATELY ISSUED. Not in Sturges, McKee, etc.

107. ROGERS (BOB). Mar's Master. A Classical Exposition of Material Influences that caused the European War. *Illustrations.* 12mo, pp. 61.
Louisville, Kentucky, 1916
    *Presentation copy to "Dorothy Milburn." I have seen every woman, but there is only one Dorothy. Bob Rogers. Chevalier Rogaire. Louisville, Ky. March 18, 1917.* A play of the "World" War.

## RARE PLAY BY THE AUTHOR OF "CHARLOTTE TEMPLE"

108. ROWSON (MRS. SUSANNA HASWELL). Slaves in Algiers; or, A Struggle for Freedom: A Play, interspersed with Songs, in three acts. By Mrs. Rowson. As performed at the New Theatres in Philadelphia and Baltimore. 16mo, pp. [11] to 72 and [2].
Philadelphia: Printed for the Author by Wrigley and Berriman, No. 149, Chestnut-Street, M,DCC,XCIV (1794)
    AN EXTREMELY RARE PLAY, CONSIDERED ONE OF THE FIRST AMERICAN OPERAS and listed as such by Sonneck in his Catalogue of Operas printed before 1800. For reproduction of title see Wegelin's *Early American Plays.* LACKING IN THE FAMOUS STURGES COLLECTION, a collection of 40 years' standing. Not in McKee. Name on title and few defects as follows: 2 leaves have rip, 2 leaves lack small portions of margins, another leaf lacks small portion of margin which has affected few words of text. In the hands of a good restorer, this will become a fine copy.

109. ROWSON (WILLIAM). Every One Has his Fault: A Comedy, in five acts, By Mrs. Inchbald. As it is performed at the New Theatre, Philadelphia. Mark'd with alterations (By permission of the Managers) By William Rowson, Prompter. 16mo, unbound, pp. [5], 6 to 75 and [1].
[Philadelphia 1794 ?]
    Not in Sturges and other notable collections.
    By the husband of Susanna Haswell Rowson, the noted author of that classic of Factory Girls, "Charlotte Temple, A Tale of Truth." Mrs. Rowson herself was one of the cast of this play (as Mrs. Placid), one of the earliest parts played by her on beginning her American dramatic career.

110. ST. CÉRAN (TULLIUS DE). Pygmalion & Galathea. A Lyric Scene. Translated from the French of the Celebrated J. J. Rousseau. By Tullius De St. Céran, Professor of the French language in this City [Baltimore]. 12mo, sewed, pp. 12.
Baltimore: Printed and Published by J. Robinson, Circulating Library and Dramatic Repository, 94, Market-street, 1823
AN EXTREMELY RARE AMERICAN PLAY. Not in Sturges, McKee, Harris, etc. This is the FIRST AMERICAN TRANSLATION of Rosseau's *Pygmalion.*

111. [SARGENT (GEORGE W.).] The Union Sergeant, or the Battle of Gettysburg, A Historical Drama of the War. Founded on facts. Written by a Veteran of the War for the Union, and respectfully dedicated to the Grand Army of the Republic. 16mo, original cloth and paper label, pp. xii, [3], 2 to 70.
Springfield, Mass: Geo. W. Sargent, Publisher, 1873
Presentation copy to Col. Thos. S. Peck. Not in Roden, Sturges, McKee, Harris or Maier.

112. SCENES AT GURNEY'S. An Ethiopian Act, as performed by The San Francisco Ministrels, New York. 16mo, original wrappers, pp. 8.
New York. Happy Hours Company . . . [186—]
Not in Sturges, McKee, Harris, Maier, etc.

113. SMITH (RICHARD PENN). The Deformed, or, Woman's Trial, A Play in five Acts . . . as performed at the Chestnut Street Theatre—Philadelphia. 12mo, original printed wrappers, pp. 87.     Philadelphia Edition, 1830
Not in Sturges or McKee collections.
Has autograph of Robert Hamilton, actor at the Chestnut Street Theatre 1836, later editor of Snowden's *Ladies Magazine,* New York. Also has autograph of John Kirby and John M. Rysly (?) who used this as a prompt book.
Smith's play and Wm. Dunlap's play, *The Italian Father,* are in some parts similar as they both used a play by Deckar for their plot.

114. SPRAGUE (ACHSA W.). The Poet and Other Poems. 8vo, cloth, pp. xxiii, [4], 4 to 304.         Boston: William White and Co. . . . 1864
The authoress was an early Lecturer on Spiritualism from Maine to Missouri, from Montreal to Baltimore. Her first discourse was given at South Reading, Vermont, July 16, 1854. The "Poet" is a 187-page dramatic poem. A SCARCE VOLUME by the Vermont Spiritualistic Author. Not in Sturges, McKee or Maier.

115. STEELE (SILAS S.). The Brazen Drum; or, the Yankee in Poland. A National Drama in Two Acts . . . 18mo, original printed wrappers, pp. 42 and leaf of Advertisements.         Philadelphia: Turner & Fisher . . . [1846]
Not in Sturges, McKee, Maier or New York Public Library collections. Steele was an Actor as well as a popular author.

116. STILLMAN (GEORGE A.). Life Real. A [Dramatic] Poem. 8vo, cloth, pp. 137.
New York: J. C. Derby . . . 1855
Not in Roden, Sturges, McKee or Maier.

117. TAYLEURE (CLIFTON W.). Horseshoe Robinson; or, The Battle of Kings Mountain. A Legendary Patriotic Drama, in three acts . . . as Performed at the American Theatres. 12mo, original printed wrappers, pp. [4] and 40, some pages waterstained.         New York, 1858
Neat stamp of "Howard Athenaeum Isaac B. Rich June 5, 1866 Boston" on several pages. The 4-page catalogue at front was missing from the copy described by Roden. Not in Sturges, McKee, etc.

118. TRICKS OF THE TIMES (THE), or, the World of Quacks; A Farce of Domestic
Origin. In two acts. 16mo, pp. 24, uncut edges, title somewhat foxed.

New York, 1819

> PRIVATELY PRINTED AND EXCESSIVELY RARE, no copy being located in the
> Sturges, McKee, Harris, or other collections consulted.
> A close reading of this play leaves an impression of its having been written by the
> "Croakers" themselves, possibly by Drake.
> Note the following extracts:—*Scene IV*—meeting of a learned society—*page 11*,
> "The thanks of the society were then returned to the doctor (Mitchill?) for his
> recondite researches, with the amendment,‖that such a daring descent was left to be
> accomplished by the American Linnaeus; *and Dr. Croaker, his biographer, requested
> to present an ode on the occasion*, at a future meeting of the Society."
> *Act II, page 19*, "Ex-Gov. Why that Croaker is a damn'd fellow. He did me more
> mischief than ———— to bring in my name with Johnny Targee, and talk at the
> same time of the *wanderer dying under the American Flag*. . . But when I was mayor,
> why didn't you get the *freedom of the city in a gold box?*" (This last underlined part
> of note is title of a poem written by Drake in the "Croaker" articles.)
> *Act II, page 24*, "Dr. San. (solus). These Croakers! An Indian warfare is kept up
> against me; I'm shot at from every bush, and not a squib or a cracker is thrown in
> the air but I am singed . . . First Dick Shift cuts between us with his chain-shot,
> that damn'd couplet; then Pindar Puff to Dick Shift, in which even my religion is
> questioned and to crown all Sir Archy to Pindar Puff, with his cursed compliments
> —'The pride of the ball'—of hell! . . . Not content, they come out in numbers;
> epistle No. 1, epistle No. 2, an arithmetical progression of burlesques, a polypus
> of libels. etc."
> Any one looking up the series of articles as written by the "Croakers" will note the
> intimate tone of reference to different parties and poems as used in the play. The
> italicized parts of the notes are the titles of poems by Drake.

## ONLY AMERICAN PLAY WITH A FULL-PAGE MASONIC DEDICATION

119. TURNBULL (JOHN D.). Rudolph, or the Robbers of Calabria; A Melo Drama,
in three Acts, with marches, combats and chorusses as performed at the
Boston Theatre. By John D. Turnbull. Of the Boston Theatre . . .
Author of the Maid of Hungary. Copyright secured according to Law.
16mo, unbound, pp. 47.

Boston: Printed by B. True, 75 State-Street, 1807

> Not in Sturges Collection. CONTAINS THE FINEST MASONIC AND ONLY MASONIC
> DEDICATION I have seen attached to any American Play especially of this early date.
> Dedicated To his Excellency General Jacob Morton, Grand Master of the most
> ancient and honorable fraternity of Free and accepted Masons of the State of New
> York. This was written in gratitude to Gen. Morton and Masonic Fraternity for
> befriending the author and securing his release from prison. A dedication written
> from the heart.

120. WHITE (WILLIAM CHARLES). The Poor Lodger; A Comedy in five acts.
By William Charles White, as performed at the Boston Theatre . . . 18mo,
unbound, pp. 90, lacks 2 leaves of Epilogue.

Boston: Printed by Joshua Belcher, 1811

> Not in Sturges, McKee, Harris, Maier or New York Public Library List. WHITE'S
> PLAYS ARE EXTREMELY RARE even in an imperfect condition.

121. WILLIAMSON (EUGENE F.). Miriam. A Drama in three scenes. Square 16mo,
original cloth, pp. 32.   Pittsburgh: Stevenson, Foster, & Co., 1879

> Not in Sturges, Harris, McKee, Maier, New York Public Library List, nor in
> Roden's *Bibliography of later American Plays*.

122. WILLIAM TELL. A Lyric Drama, in three acts. By M. Pelissier, Music by
Gretry. Translated literally, for the use of Visitors to the French Opera.
From an authentic copy, by permission of the Manager of the New Orleans
Opera Company. Translated by W. P. W. 16mo, unbound, pp. 47.

Baltimore: Published by E. J. Coale . . . 1831

Unknown to Roden. An American play of which I can TRACE No Copy. Lacking
in all the notable catalogues of American Poetry and Plays,—Sturges, McKee,
Harris, etc.


123. WILLIS (NATHANIEL PARKER). Two Ways of Dying for a Husband. I. Dying
to Keep Him, or, Tortesa the Usher. II. Dying to Lose Him, or, Bianca
Visconti. 8vo, boards, leather title-label, pp. [9], 2 to 245, and [2 of adver-
tisements], uncut edges. London: Hugh Cunningham . . . 1839

Played at the National Theatre, New York, 1839, James H. Wallack taking the
part of Tortesa. Roden mentions the above edition and states it to be VERY SCARCE,
not having seen a copy he gives no collation or full title. Not in Sturges, McKee
or New York Public Library catalogues.


## BY THE AUTHOR OF THE "OLD OAKEN BUCKET"

124. WOODWORTH (SAMUEL). The Widow's Son, or, Which is the Traitor. A
Melo-Drama, in three Acts, As performed at the New York Park Theatre
. . . Music By J. H. Swindells, of New York . . . 16mo, sewed, pp. 82,
EDGES UNCUT AND MOST PAGES UNOPENED.
New-York: Published at the Circulating Library and Dramatic Repository,

No. 4 Chambers-St. . . . 1825

This play of the American Revolution contains a fine seven-page introduction
giving a history of the plot of the play as based upon historical facts. Among the
characters introduced we have Gen. Clinton, Gen. Washington, Maj. Arnold, Sergt.
André, Gen. Lee and Sergeant Edward Champe who seems the character most
spoken of in the play. Portions of margins on 2 pages gone but VERY RARE IN AN
UNCUT AND UNOPENED CONDITION. Autograph of John McCullough the noted
American Tragedian and San Francisco Theatrical Manager written across title.


125. WRIGHT (CALEB EARL). Frances Slocum; The Lost Sister. A Poem; [AND,
bound in,] Sidney Leah. A Metrical Romance. 2 vols. in one, 8vo, cloth,
pp. 43 and 128.
Wilkes-Barre, Pa.: Robert Baur & Son, Printers and Publishers, 1889

"Frances Slocum" is an Indian Captivity in Verse; and "Sidney Leah" is a Play.
Not in Roden, Sturges, McKee, Maier or New York Public Library.


## PRESENTATION COPY OF A RARE PLAY BY FRANCES WRIGHT
## A GIFT TO WILLIAM DUNLAP

126. WRIGHT (FRANCES). Altorf. A Tragedy. First represented in the Theatre
of New York. Feb. 19, 1819. 12mo, contemporary boards, roan back,
pp. Title leaf, page to the reader, numbered v, [4 unnumbered], and 6 to
83.
Philadelphia: Published by M. Carey & Son, No. 126 Chestnut-Street, 1819

THIS COPY IS PERFECT although numbered oddly. It evidently contains more
pages than the New York Public Library copy and begins 6 to 83 instead of 5 to 83
as called for in their collation. The authoress evidently had some change made
which caused the confusion in pagination. Not in Sturges.

# AMERICAN VERSE PRINTED IN A BROADSIDE FORM

The rarity of this particular form of American Verse need not be dwelt upon. It has ever been the fault of the average human being to overlook the real value of a printed leaflet or sheet, on account of its non-imposing appearance, when at the same time the worthless volume with a fine gilt binding has been kept. "Throw it away, it's no good," has been the motto, where Broadsides were concerned. Therefore their present rarity, for which this generation must pay.

## A BLOODY BATTLE

Between the United States Troops under the command of Gov Harrison, and several tribes of Indians, near the Prophet's town, Nov. 7th, 1811.

O'ER western hills, Columbia's martial band
March'd forth to guard her own defenceless land,
From savage inrodes, on her new frontiers,
To defend the people, and allay their fears.

Harrison, a commander of great renown,
Led on our troops near by the Prophet's town.
After toils o'ercome, and obstructions past,
Near this savage town they encamp'd at last.

November the seventh, before 'twas light,
Those Indian tribes began a bloody fight.
Dark was the hour, and gloomy all around,
When horrid yells from savage tribes did sound.

The dreadful war-hoop roar'd inceffantly,
Which plainly did foretell some mischief nigh;
Then on our troops they rush'd with fiercest rage,
Was quickly form'd their ranks, did them engage.

Still preffing on, like heroes they did fight,
They charg'd those tribes, and put them all to flight.
Their tomahawks they us'd in firm array,
Yet to our gallant troops they soon gave way

What carnage's seen—the dead confused lye,
Our troops and savage men both mix and die.
And garments roll'd in blood, stood full in view,
Caus'd by that base—that wicked Indian crew

How many youths that left their native shore,
Their dearest friends—alas! are now no more.
Oh! we lament so many met their doom,
Now to the field, and heroes in the bloom.

Columbia's heroic band'r her pride and boast,
And they who speak the truest, praise them most,
Their great exploits appear sublimely bright,
Shine in their native, not a borrow'd light.

EDWARD, An American Soldier.

NED oft' had brav'd the field of battle,
Had oft' endur'd the hardest woe;
Had been where deep-mouth'd cannons rattle
And oft' been captur'd by the foe.

His heart was kind, to fear a stranger,
Columbia's cause was his pride;
He nobly scorn'd to shrink from danger,
And on a bed of honor dy'd.

For, fays Ned, whate'er befalls,
An American scorns to whine,
He'll cheerful go where duty calls,
And brave all ills but ne'er repine:

Ned lov'd sincere his charming Kitty,
She saw with tears her soldier go,
She pray'd kind heav'n to lend her pity,
And shield her Edward from the foe

My love, he cry'd, my grief give vent;
Those tears disgrace a soldier's brow
But hapless Kitty lost her lover,
Who on a bed of honor dy'd.

For, for fays Ned, whate'er befalls,
An American scorns to whine,
He'll cheerful go where duty calls,
And brave all ills but ne'er repine.

[No. 128]

## UNIQUE GERMAN-AMERICAN POETICAL BROADSIDE POEM

127. AUF DEN TOD des entschlasenen Vater Muhlenbergs. *48-line poem, printed within ornamental borders.* Small 4to.
[Philadelphia: Gedrucht bey Melchior Steiner, in den Rees-strasse, zwischen den Zweyten- und Dritten-strasse. [1787]

Lacking in Sturges collection and all Bibliographies and catalogues on the subject.
As this was issued the same time as Helmuth's sermon on the death of Dr. Muhlenberg, in which part of this poem is reprinted, without question the above must have been printed by the same source, therefore Steiner's full imprint as on Sermon is given. No other copy has been traced in Seidensticker's First Century of German Printing in America—Nor in Evans, or any authority on poetical works. The above was printed without doubt to be sung at the Church Services in 1787.
See also under Helmuth, No. 449.

## "A BLOODY BATTLE" [IN INDIANA TERRITORY]

128. BETWEEN THE UNITED STATES TROOPS under the command of Gov. Harrison, and several tribes of Indians, near the Prophet's town, Nov. 7th, 1811; [AND] Edward, an American Soldier (the 2 on one sheet). 4to, mounted and bound in half morocco covers.  No place [1811]

> Not in Sturges, Harris, McKee, Maier or New York Public Library.
> Verse two begins:—"Harrison, a commander of great renown,
> Led on our troops near by the Prophets Town,
> After Toils o'ercome and obstructions past
> Near this savage town they encamp'd at last."
> Verse three:— "November the seventh, before 'twas light,
> Those Indian tribes began a bloody fight" etc.
> Broadside poems on the "Battle of Tippecanoe," in the Territory of Indiana, are almost unique when obtainable. Probably printed in the West, judging from the paper used.

[See facsimile]

129. CALIFORNIA. A Poem by a Resident of California. *40-line verse.*
San Francisco: R. Benicia, April, 1849. N. Flickman, Printer

> Evidently the first poem written describing the delights of living in California and the West. Not in Sturges, etc.

130. DYING CALIFORNIAN, THE. *32-line verse.* 8vo.
Boston: Horace Partridge, [1855?]

> See under *Songsters* for "Dying Californian" poem set to music. Not in Sturges, etc.

## A HITHERTO UNRECORDED POETICAL BROADSIDE
## PRINTED IN BOSTON IN 1738

131. DYING LAMENTATION (THE) and Advice of Philip Kennison, who was executed at Cambridge in New-England (for burglary) on Friday, the 15th Day of September 1738: In the 28th Year of his age. All written by his own hand, a few days before his death; and published at his earnest desire, for the good of survivors. Folio, mounted (a very few slight defects), beautifully bound in full Spanish mottled calf, BY SANGORSKI & SUTCLIFFE. [Colophon.] Boston, Printed and sold at the Heart and Crown, in Cornhill: where may be had a Narrative of his life, written by his own hand [1738]

> THIS BROADSIDE IS UNIQUE. It is not mentioned in the newly issued bibliography of Broadsides, Ballads, etc., printed in Massachusetts before 1800. Evans mentions the Narrative of his life, but not this broadside. Not in Wegelin, Sturges, McKee, Maier, New York Public Library, Sabin, Otis, Onderdonk or any other authority consulted.

[See Frontispiece for facsimile]

132. ENGLISH (JOSIAH GIBERTON, of Xenia, Ohio). Poetical leaflets as follows:—
I—"Song of God in Man Not Singing Flame;" II—"Must be Seen and Felt to be Understood;" III—"In Memory of the Fiftieth Anniversary of Mr. and Mrs. E. C. Stiles, Jefferson City, Missouri, July 7, 1886;" IV—"Moontide Exit," Xenia, O., Sept. 1888; V—"Moontide Exit," words and music, 1888. Together, 5 pieces, 16mo, 12mo, and 8vo.
Xenia, Ohio, 1880–1886–1888–1889

> A rare lot of PRIVATELY PRINTED ITEMS by this Ohio author. Not in Sturges, or similar collections.

133. [FOSTER (STEPHEN C.).] Oh! Boys Carry Me 'Long, as sung by the Celebrated New Orleans Opera and Ballet Troupe, in all the principal cities in the U. S., With great applause. Copyright secured. *48 lines of verse, printed within an ornamental border.* 8vo.
Thomas M. Scroggy, Publisher, Card & Fancy Job Printer . . . Philadelphia, no date
    Rare original broadside issue with copyright notice. Not in Sturges, etc.

134. FOSTER (STEPHEN C.). That's What's the Matter. *Colored portrait and view at top of sheet.* 8vo.        New York, Charles Magnus [186–]
    Civil War Song, by the most popular ballad writer the United States has produced. Not in Sturges, etc. (For other Foster items see under *Songsters.*)

135. FOSTER (STEPHEN C.). Was My Brother in the Battle? By C. S. [*i. e.*, S. C.] Foster. *Colored battle scene at top.* 8vo.
New York and Washington, D. C.: Charles Magnus [1861]
    Not in Sturges, etc.

136. FOSTER (STEPHEN C.). We've a Million in the Field. Written and composed by Stephen C. Foster. *Volunteer at home camp scene, in colors at top.* 8vo.
New York and Washington, D. C.: Charles Magnus [186–]
    Not in Sturges, etc.

137. GENERIC NAMES, For the Country and People of the United States of America. Folio, printed in double columns of type with the title as given on above first 2 lines.        No place or printer [1811?]
    A unique and curious broadside advocating the use of a poetic name for the United States and poetic names for its People. Not in Sturges, McKee, Harris, Maier or New York Public Library.
    The author says the radical word "Fredonia" is also well adapted to songs and rhymes. And this is a great convenience and felicity in a national point of view, observe how prettily our poets can make it jingle; for instance if the subject is warlike, then,

          "Their Chiefs to glory lead on,
          The Noble Sons of Fredon."
Or if it is Moral sublimity,
          "Nor Plato, in his Phaedon,
          Excels the Sage of Fredon."
Should it be Commercial Activity,
          "All Nations have agreed on
          The Enterprise of Fredon" etc. etc.

138. GRAY (JANE). Sunday Institute—Lecture Room Museum. Poem by Miss Jane Gray, Sung by the Choir on the occasion of opening the Institute for the Season, Sunday Evening, October 2, 1853. Narrow folio.
No place, 1853
    Not in Sturges, etc.

139. HARMON (A. W.). Columbia Mourns for Maj. Gen. Hiram G. Berry, Who Fell in the Battle of Chancellorsville. Composed by A. W. Harmon. 8vo.
No place, or printer [186–]
    Not in Sturges, etc.

140. HARMON (A. W.). Georgianna Lovering or, the Northwood Tragedy! Composed by A. W. Harmon. *112 lines of verse printed within an ornamental border.*
No place, or printer [186–]
[*Continued*

Description in verse of the murder of Georgianna Lovering of Northwood, N. H., by her Uncle, Franklin B. Evans. Somewhat broken in folds. Not in Sturges, etc.

141. HARVARD COLLEGE. Carmen Seculare: In lingua Latina forcelliana compositium, et in canticum Nov-Anglis pergratum, Yankeedoodledandium, accommodatum. Licentia poetica frequentissime ursurpata, calamo currente scripsit Gulielmus Magnushumilis.
Die Septembris VIII, Anno Salutis, MDCCCXXXVI. Collegiique Harvardini Fundati CC.
Original Harvard poem, sung to the tune of Yankee Doodle. AN EXTREMELY RARE BROADSIDE. Not in Sturges, etc.

142. HOLMES (OLIVER WENDELL). Order of Exercises at the Boston Music Hall, On Saturday Evening, February 4th, 1865, to celebrate the progress of Freedom's Great Work in the United States of America . . . Hymn written for the Occasion by Oliver Wendell Holmes. *20 lines of verse.* Folio.
Boston: Wright & Potter, Printers, 4 Spring Lane [1865]
EXTREMELY RARE FIRST EDITION of Oliver Wendell Holmes. Lacking in the Chamberlain, Arnold, Maier, Foote, Roos, Harris, Sturges, McKee and other sales.

143. LINCOLN (ABRAHAM). The Nation Mourns. *Printed in black and white with inset portrait of Lincoln at top.* 8vo. [New York] Chas. Magnus [1865]
RARE. Not in Sturges, etc. For other rare Lincoln death Songs see under *Songsters.*

144. OLD TIPPECANOE. The "Log Cabin"—Log Cabin and Hard Cider Song—Our Hero Farmer. Folio, stitched in folds where broken.
[Old Milford, Mass., 1845]
Rare Harrison for President Song Sheet. Not in Sturges, etc. No place, date or printer.

145. PETER GRAY. An Affecting Song on the Sorrowful Death of Peter Gray and Lizzie Anna Querl. *Printed within ornamental borders.*
New York: J. Andrews, Printer, 38 Chatham St. [184–?]
RARE. The sad fate of Peter Gray is related as follows:—
"A trading he went to the West,
For Furs and other skins,
And there he was in crimson drest,
By Bloody In-ji-ins."
Not in Sturges, etc.

146. RAILROAD BOY'S APPEAL (A). On account of being maimed, I offer for sale this song to obtain an artificial limb, whereby I will be able to secure some kind of employment. *32 lines of verse, printed within an ornamental border.* 8vo. No place, or printer [187–]
An interesting example of "Beggar's Poetry." Not in Sturges, etc.

147. SONG for the Abbot Jubilee. [Exeter, N. H.], August 23, 1838. *32 lines of verse.* 8vo. No place or printer [Exeter, 1838]
In pencil is written "by S. S. F.—"(?) Not in Sturges, etc.

148. SOUTHERN CHIVALRY. Dedicated to Anson Burlingame. Folio.
No place [186–]
Not in Sturges, etc.

149. [ST. JOHN (PETER OR SAMUEL).]. American Taxation. Small folio, untrimmed edges.    No place, or printer [1778]

Not in Sturges, McKee, Harris, or New York Public Library catalogues.

The above broadside was issued under three different titles as follows, "Taxation of America," "British Taxation of North America," and "American Taxation," as above. Duyckinck lists title as above offered. Moore lists the "Taxation of America" edition. The above offered edition and the "British Taxation of North America" edition are identical in text, although title has been changed. The Duyckinck and Moore copies differ somewhat in text from the present copy. See: *Illustrated Catalogue of Historical Americana*, sold April 22, 1919, for companion copy to above, and Duyckinck and Moore for the other text. Duyckinck gives Samuel of New Canaan, Conn., and Moore gives Peter of Norwalk, Conn., as the author. The buyer will have to take his choice of authors.

[See facsimile]

### AMERICAN TAXATION.

[No. 149]

150. SUNDAY INSTITUTE, Lecture Room, Museum. Hymn sung at Concert Hall, on the occasion of a Lecture by the Rev. J. Chambers. The Bible the Light of the World [Verse]; [AND] A Paraphrase by Miss Jane Gray, Sung at the Museum on the occasion of a review of Mr. Chambers' Lecture. Narrow folio.    No place, or printer [1853]

Not in Sturges, etc.

151. [WEEKS (A. W.).] In Memory of Charles Warren Weeks, who sleeps in the Cerro Gordo County Cemetery, State of Iowa. He fell asleep exposed to a violent snowstorm. December 22, 1855, aged 23 years, 7 months and 10 days. *8 lines of verse printed in large type*, signed A. W.[eeks]. 4to.

No place, 1855

Not in Sturges, etc.

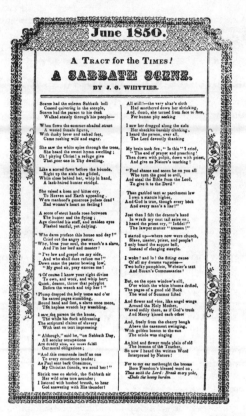

[No. 152]

## THE ONLY COPY KNOWN OF A BROADSIDE POEM BY WHITTIER

152. WHITTIER (JOHN GREENLEAF). A Tract for the Times! A Sabbath Scene. Original Broadside Poem of *27 stanzas of 4 lines each, printed in double columns*. Small folio, enclosed in a cloth case. No place, June, 1850

EXTREMELY RARE. The Arnold copy, with bookplate. In Arnold's collection this was catalogued as the ONLY COPY KNOWN.

Not in Sturges, McKee or any other source consulted except Arnold.

[See facsimile]

153. ADVENTURES (THE) of Old Dame Trudge and her Parrott. *Illustrated with Whimsical Engravings* IN COLORS. Small 4to, original printed wrappers, 8 leaves, printed on one side only.

Philadelphia: Published and sold Wholesale by Wm. Charles, No. 32, South Third Street, and may be had of all the Booksellers. Price 18¾ cents. 1817

> RARE. With the exception of front wrapper showing discoloration by water, this is in exceptionally fine condition for a child's poetical work. The back wrapper lists 30 works of this kind with number of plates making a nice little check list for bibliographical purposes. Not in Sturges, McKee, Harris, Maier or New York Public Library.

### RARE JUVENILE WORK OF POETICAL INTEREST

154. METAMORPHOSIS; or, a Transformation of Pictures, with Poetical Explanations for the Amusement of Young Persons. *Folding plates, woodcuts by J. Poupard.* 18mo.

New-York: Sold by Samuel Wood and Sons, No. 261, Pearl Street. Printed by J. Rakestraw, Philadelphia, 1820

> Not in Sturges, McKee, Harris, Maier or New York Public Library.
> RARE AND CHOICE COPY. The plates change Adam into Eve, Lions into queer Eagles, etc. The first rhyme begins:—
> "Adam comes first upon the stage,
> And Eve from out his side,
> Who was given him in marriage;
> Turn up and see the bride."
> By turning up half the plate we then see the bride, Eve.

### "MOTHER GOOSE'S MELODIES," 1833, WITH A HIT AT THE "BOOK OF MORMON"

155. MOTHER GOOSE'S MELODIES. The only Pure Edition containing all that have ever come to light of her Memorable Writings, together with those which have been discovered among the Mss. of Herculaneum. Likewise every one found in the same stone box which holds the Golden Plates of the Book of Mormon. The Whole Compared, Revised, and Sanctioned by one of The Annotators of the Goose Family. *With many new engravings* . . . Square 16mo, full rough-grained morocco, original wrappers preserved, pp. 96.     Boston: Printed and Published by Munroe and Francis [1833]

> Not in Sturges, McKee, Maier, Harris, etc.
> As is usual with this rare work for Children, some pages have been mended and the original wrappers which are well worn have been mounted on stiff paper, waterstained and showing time discoloration. A perfect copy in text of this work.

156. MY TIPPOO. A Poem. Small 4to, original printed wrappers, worn. 6 leaves *with colored engravings* depicting the life and heroic actions of Tippoo from Puppy to Doghood.     Philadelphia: . . . Wm. Charles [1810?]

> The date has worn off but is around the period of 1810.
> RARE. Inside plates are clean although edges have curled from use which is but natural with children's books. Not in Sturges, McKee, Harris, Maier or New York Public Library.

157. NEW-YORK CRIES in Rhyme. *Woodcuts.* 16mo, original printed wrappers, pp. 24 including covers.   New York: Mahlon Day, 374 Pearl Street. 1836

[*Continued*

A RARE AND FINE COPY. Contains a description of New-York, and woodcuts illustrating the cries to the following occupations:—"Mats! Mats!"—"Baskets! Wooden Bowls!"—"Cherries!"—"Water Melons!"—"Pine Apples!"—"New Milk!"—"Sand O!"—"Beans, Peas, etc.!"—"Scissors to Grind!"—"Potatoes, O.!"—"Brooms! Brooms!"—"Hot Corn!"—"Radishes!"—"Matches!"—"Oranges!"—"Sweep O!"—"Straw-Berries!"—"Clams! Clams!"—"Locks or Keys!" With an account of each trade underneath.

This 1836 edition not in Sturges, McKee, Harris or Maier.

158. PHILADELPHIA CRIES. *Woodcuts.* Small 4to, pp. [12].

Philadelphia, Boston, New York, Baltimore: Fisher & Brother [184–?]

SCARCE. The woodcuts are crudely colored. Contains Cries of the following trades:—Flower Girl, Old Clothes, Ballad Singer, Buy a Broom, Ripe Cherries, Sweep, Oh, Oh, Oh!, Milk Below, Hot Corn, Dolls to Sell, etc. etc. Picture of Napoleon Bonaparte on the Island of St. Helena, etc. Not in Sturges, McKee, Harris, Maier or New York Public Library.

159. THINK BEFORE YOU SPEAK: or, The Three Wishes. A Tale [in verse]. By the author of the Peacock at home. *6 copperplates.* Small 4to, sewed, pp. 32.

Philadelphia: Published by Johnson & Warner, No. 147, Market Street,
J. Bouvier, Printer, 1810

RARE. *Charles M. Reeds, Oct. 31 1826* written on top of title. Not in Sturges, McKee, Harris, Maier or New York Public Library.

160. WHIMSICAL INCIDENTS; or, the Power of Music. A Poetic Tale by a near Relation of Old Mother Hubbard. *Copperplate engravings, colored by hand.* Very small 4to, 32 unnumbered leaves, besides the 2 fly-leaves and original wrappers.              No place, no date [Year 1810 written on title]

AN EXCESSIVELY RARE CHILD'S POETICAL WORK with curious and interesting copperplate illustrations hand colored. Printed on one side of leaf only. As is usual with works of this kind it shows use by time, being somewhat stained, and wrappers, becoming brittle have chipped in spots, nevertheless a good copy.

Not in Sturges, McKee, Harris, Maier or New York Public Library.

## SONGSTERS, ETC.

Almost all items under this heading were lacking in the Sturges and other mentioned collections, whether so stated or not. This is a species of verse which most collections lack and yet a glance over their contents would show their desirability in any poetry collection. The Library of Congress, Harvard University (Wendell Collection), University of Texas (Bieber Collection), and the Grosvenor Library have quite a collection of this type of verse. The Harris Collection is strong on Songsters and Ballad Sheets, but lacks all the fine American Poems which were set to Music. For an interesting discovery among the Music Sheet items see under Longfellow, No. 515. The wise Librarian and Collector will follow the above tip, and get American-Written items of this type, while the getting is still fairly good. The writer knows for a fact that this sort of item is becoming rarer every day. Look the Booksellers' stocks over, and see how few items you will find that contain poems and songs of American Origin.

### RARE AMERICAN MINIATURE SONGSTER

161. AEOLIAN HARP (THE), or, Songster's Cabinet; being a selection of the most popular Songs and Recitations, Patriotic, Sentimental, Humorous, &c. Size 2 by 2½ inches, bound in full old roan, pp. 124 and [4] of index.

Philadelphia: Published by S. Hart & Son, 1829

[ *Continued*

[ No. 161. AEOLIAN HARP—*Continued* ]
>Contains many little-known Songs of the American Revolution, War of 1812, etc.
Some of the titles are as follows:—"The Hornet Triumphant; or Victory No. 5;"
"Death of Warren;" "Saratoga and Morgiana;" "American Captive;" "Yankee Chron-
ology," by Dunlap; "Siege of Plattsburg;" "Ode to Printing;" "I need not tell thee," by
Wm. Dunlap; "Epilogue to the Soldier's Daughter," by John Howard Payne; etc. etc.

162. AIRS OF THE PILGRIMS. 16mo, cloth, pp. 76.                     [Plymouth, 1846?]
>The preface is signed W. S. R.  A very valuable collection of Pilgrim's Songs and
Verse; includes:—A Word to Boston; A Word to New England, by Gov. Wm.
Bradford, written before 1649; Poetical Description of Fish and Trees in New
England, written 1639; New England Hymn, by Matthew Byles, 1770; Whaling
Song, by John Osborne, before 1787; and many other interesting articles.

163. AMERICAN MOCK-BIRD; or, Cabinet of Anacreon, being A Selection of the
Most Elegant and Fashionable Songs; sung in the Anacreontic and Phil-
harmonic Societies, and in most genteel circles, with A Number of Choice
Masonic Songs and Sentiments. 12mo, old calf, pp. 258, [6].
New-York: Published by David Longworth, at the Shakespeare Gallery,
No. 11, Park, 1801
>RARE MASONIC AND FASHIONABLE SONGSTER. Not in Harris collection list. Con-
tains also Patriotic Songs: "America Commerce and Freedom;" "The Indian Death
Song;" "Columbia;" etc. Pages are shaky in binding and one is ripped.

164. AMERICAN MUSICAL MISCELLANY (THE): A Collection of the Newest and
Most Approved Songs, Set to Music. [8 lines verse.] 12mo, old tree calf,
pp. 300.
Printed at Northampton, Massachusetts.  By Andrew Wright for Daniel
Wright and Company . . . 1798
>"To All True Lovers of Song in the United States of Columbia this Volume is
humbly dedicated by the Publishers." Contains:—"Columbia, Columbia, to Glory
Rise," by Dr. Dwight; "Adams and Liberty," by T. (Robt. T.) Paine; "The Hobbies"
(the American has long been known, "Their Hobby is Washington, Peace and Free
Trade;" "Rise Columbia," by T. (Robt. T.) Paine; "The Indian Chief;" "Hail America
Hail;" "Song LI." Written by Thomas Dawes, Jun. Esquire, and Sung at the Entertainment given on Bunker's Hill by the Proprietor of Charles River Bridge, at the
opening of the same, etc. A RARE, INTERESTING AND VALUABLE COLLECTION OF
OLD TIME SONGS.

165. AMERICAN (THE) Naval and Patriotic Songster; As sung at various places
of Amusement, in honor of Hull, Jones, Decatur, Perry, Bainbridge, Lawrence, &c., &c., &c. "Don't give up the Ship." By * * * * * * * *. *Plates*,
32mo, original cloth and title label, pp. 256.                     Baltimore, 1836
>VERY RARE PRIVATELY PRINTED War of 1812 songster. Contains the following
plates:—"Battle of Lake Erie;" "The Hornet and Peacock;" "The Constitution and
Guerrier;" "Bombardment of Fort McHenry, Baltimore;" and another cut without
title. A Fine Collection.

166. BALLADS of the War. Large 4to. Wrappers and 13 leaves.
No place or printer [1875]
>Facsimile copies of the original manuscript poems, "Brother Jonathan's Lament
for Sister Caroline," by O. W. Holmes, 1875; "Battle Hymn of the Republic," by
J. W. Howe; "The Cumberland," by H. W. Longfellow; "Barbara Fritchie," by John
G. Whittier, 1875; "Death of Lincoln," by Wm. C. Bryant, 1875. Not in Sturges,
Bryant Bibliography, nor in his Collection sold at auction in 1912. Not in McKee,
Arnold, Foote, Roos, Harris or Maier collections.

167. BARLOW (JOEL). Doctor Watts' Imitation of the Psalms of David, corrected and enlarged by Joel Barlow. To which is added, a Collection of Hymns; The whole applied to the State of the Christian Church in General. 12mo, old calf, pp. 348 and [24 of Index, Tables, etc.]
Glasgow: Printed by David Niven: For James Duncan, Bookseller, Trongate. MDCCLXXXVI (1786)
Not in Sturges, McKee, Harris, Maier or New York Public Library catalogues.

168. BELKNAP (JEREMY). Sacred Poetry, consisting of Psalms and Hymns, adapted to Christian Devotion, in Public and Private    . Second Edition, with Improvements. Published according to Act of Congress. Thick 18mo, original calf, pp. 231, [10] and 2 to 263.
Printed at Boston, For Thomas & Andrews, and D. West (Proprietors of the Work). Sold by them at their respective Bookstores, and by the several Booksellers in Town and Country, Nov., 1797
RARE SECOND EDITION. The earliest edition listed in Harris catalogue is 1804. Not in Sturges, Harris, McKee, Maier or New York Public Library catalogues.

169. BRYANT'S ESSENCE OF OLD VIRGINNY, containing all the New, Fashionable and Laughable Negro Songs, as sung by the celebrated Bryant's Minstrels. *Woodcuts and frontispiece portraits of the Bryant Brothers.* 18mo, original printed wrappers, pp. 72.    New York: Robert M. DeWitt [1857]
FINE COPY of a scarce and well-printed Songster.

170. BRYANT'S SONGS FROM DIXIE'S LAND, containing all the New, Laughable, Humorous, Comic and Fashionable Songs and Melodies of that popular Band of Ethiopian Performers, The Bryant Brothers. *View of Bryant's Mechanics Hall on back wrapper.* 18mo, original printed wrappers, pp. 72.
New York: Robert M. DeWitt . . . [1861]

171. BRUCE (CHARLES). Poems, Songs, and Ballads of the Sea, and Celebrated Discoverers, Battles, Shipwrecks, and Incidents, illustrative of Life on the Sea, Compiled and arranged by Charles Bruce. *Illustrations.* 8vo, original cloth, pp. XVI, [3], 4 to 399, 16.
London and Edinburgh: William P. Nimmo, 1878
VERY SCARCE. The American authors represented are Freneau, Harte, Aldrich, Longfellow, T. B. Read, G. D. Prentice, Epes Sargent, J. G. C. Brainard, Ellet, etc. At the end pasted on the leaves of advertisements are additional Poems and Songs. Not in Sturges, McKee, Harris or Maier.

172. BUNKER HILL SONGSTER. Containing National and Patriotic Songs. As sung by the Principal Vocalists. *Woodcuts.* 32mo, original printed wrappers, pp. 34.
[Boston]: Murphy, Printer and Publisher. Franklin Book Store. [184-?]
FINE COPY. Contains "The Green Mountain Boys," by Wm. Cullen Bryant. Not in Harris, Sturges, etc.

173. BURTON (WILLIAM E.—Comedian). Billy Burton's Comic Songster; being entirely a new collection of Original and Popular Songs, as sung by Mr. Burton, Mr. Tyrone Power, Mr. John Reeve, Mr. Hadaway, &c., &c. *With twelve engravings.* 32mo, cloth, pp. 262.
New York: Philip J. Cozans . . . 1860
By the Noted Actor and Theatrical Manager. Not in the Harris collection of Songsters.

174. CHANTS, OCCASIONAL PIECES, and Plain Tunes for the use of the Protestant
Episcopal Churches in the United States. 8vo, original boards, pp. [4],
1 to 63, [1].                          Salem: Printed by Joshua Cushing, 1814
Not in Harris Songster collection, etc. VERY UNCOMMON.

175. CHOICE SELECTION (A) of Hymns and Spiritual Songs, designed to aid in the
Devotions of Prayer, Conference, and Camp-Meetings. "Let the inhabitants of the rock sing." 32mo, original boards, pp. 159.
                          Windsor, Vt. Published by N. C. Goddard, 1836
Not in Gilman, Harris, etc. The verse on the title is very appropriate for Vermonters. A SCARCE CAMP-MEETING SONGSTER.

176. CHRISTY'S MELODIES [Carry Me Back to Old Virginia] as composed and Sung
by them at their Concerts with distinguished success. *Portraits of Christy
in Character lithographed in a greenish tint and black and white.* Large 4to,
pp. 5.                          New York: Jaques & Brother, 1847

177. CHRISTY'S PANORAMA SONGSTER; containing the Songs as sung by The Christy,
Campbell, Pierce's Minstrels and Sabel Brothers. *Woodcut illustrations.*
16mo, original printed wrappers, pp. [2], 71 to 134 and 2.
                          New York: William H. Murphy, *circa* 1846
SCARCE MINSTREL SONGSTER.

178. [CLAY (HENRY).] The Ashland Melodies. Written by "An Old Coon" and
respectfully dedicated to J. L. Dimmock, Esq. President of Boston Clay
Club, No. 1, by the Publisher. [No. I. Here's to you Harry Clay.] *Portrait.* Large 4to, pp. 5.     Boston: Published by Henry Prentiss . . .[1844]
Rare and beautiful full-length portrait of Henry Clay on title lithographed in
black and white by Thayer & Co. "Clay for President" Song.

179. [CLAY (HENRY).] The Clay Minstrel; or, National Songster, to which is pre-
fixed A Sketch of the Life, Public Services, and Character of Henry Clay.
*Illustrated.* 18mo, unbound, pp. 167 and [1]. New York: Turner & Fisher, 1842
"Henry Clay for President" Songster.

180. [CLAY (HENRY).] Hurrah for Harry Clay. The Farmers' and Mechanicks'
Whig Song. Air, Lucy Neal. As sung with shouts of applause by George W.
Dixon, at the Meetings of the Knickerbocker Club. Large 4to, pp. 3.
                          New York: Atwill [1844]
Rare "Henry Clay for President" Song.

181. [CLAY (HENRY).] Oh, Coony, Coony Clay, A Favorite Democratic Song and
Chorus, as Sung with Unbounded Applause by the President and Mem-
bers of the Empire Club. Large 4to, pp. 3.     New York: Atwill [1844]
Anti-"Henry Clay for President" Song.

182. COOPER (GEORGE). The Men of '76. Centennial Song and Chorus. Words by
George Cooper, Music by Harrison Millard. *Lithographic view of Gen.
Washington directing his troops crossing the* [Delaware?] *River.* Large 4to,
6 pp.       Jersey City, N. J.: Published by W. H. Ewald & Bro. . . 1875
A rare Jersey City Music Sheet.

183. DWIGHT (TIMOTHY—President of Yale College). The Psalms of David . . .
A New Edition in which the Psalms omitted by Dr. Watts are versified,
local passages are altered, a number of Psalms versified anew in proper
metre. At the request of the General Association of Connecticut. To the
Psalms is added A Selecton of Hymns. *Engraved portrait of Dwight.* 32mo,
full morocco, pp. 505, and half title.      New Haven: N. Whiting, 1827
    In a fine specimen of early American black and gilt morocco binding with name of
Mary A. Treat stamped on front cover. Not in Sturges, McKee, Harris or Maier
collections.

184. DYING CALIFORNIAN (THE), or the Brother's Request, Ballad, Poetry from
the New England Diadem. Music by A. L. Lee. 4to, 5 pp.
                                                         Boston, 1855
    Not in Sturges, etc.

185. EGGLESTON (GEORGE CARY). American War Ballads and Lyrics. A Collection of the Songs and Ballads of the Colonial Wars. The Revolution, The
War of 1812–15, The War with Mexico and the Civil War. 2 vols. 16mo,
cloth and boards.
    New York and London: G. Putnam's Sons. The Knickerbocker Press
                                                              [1889]
    FIRST EDITION. SCARCE and interesting compilation. Not in Sturges, McKee or
Maier.

186. FINE KENTUCKY GENTLEMAN, air The Fine Old English Gentleman. The
Words by A Gentleman from South Carolina, inscribed To the Men who
dare to decide a Case upon its merits, The Unbiased Yeomanry of the
Country, Music by Henry Russell. Large 4to, pp. 3.
                                      New York: Firth & Hall, [1844]
    VERY RARE. Judging from the historical questions involved and mentioned in
this song, the "Fine Kentucky Gentleman" mentioned as settling same was Henry
Clay, Missouri Compromise, John of Caroline (Calhoun) and Nullification, etc.

187. FITZ (ASA) AND GREENE (J. W.). School Songs for the Million! Consisting of
Selections from the popular airs with Original Poetry. Also Original Music
. . . also A New System of Figured Music, . . . 8vo, original printed
wrappers, pp. 64.      Boston: Fitz, Hobbs & Co., 1851
    Very scarce New England Song Book with separate title to the New System of
Figured Music. Not in Harris collection of Songsters, Sturges, etc.

188. FORMAN (J. G.). Soldiers' Manual of Devotion, . . . and a collection of
Hymns and National Songs. For the Use of Chaplains and Soldiers in the
Army. 18mo, cloth, pp. 182 and [9].
    Alton, Illinois: Printed by L. A. Parks & Co., Telegraph Office, 1861
    RARE. The Arnold copy with book-label, also label of the author, Chaplain
Lyon Regiment, 3rd. Missouri Volunteers. Pasted on fly-leaf is poem clipping,
"Flag of the Red, White and Blue, additional Verses to an Old Song by Rev. J. G.
Forman."

189. FOSTER (ROBERT). A New Selection of Reformation Melodies. 24mo, sewed,
    pp. 24.    Portsmouth [N. H.]: Printed at the Christian Herald Office, 1828
    Name on verso of title. Some of the melodies are set to music. RARE.

190. FOSTER (STEPHEN C.). Beadle's Dime Song Book, No. 7, A Collection of New and Popular Comic and Sentimental Songs, comprising the latest and best productions of Stephen C. Foster. 18mo, boards, back gone, pp. 73, [7].     New York: Irwin P. Beadle & Co., No. 141 William Street [1860]
VERY SCARCE FOSTER AND BEADLE ITEM. Not in Harris Songster collection list.

191. FOSTER (STEPHEN C.). Come Where My Love Lies Dreaming. The beautiful quartette. Words and Music by Stephen C. Foster, arranged as a Song with Piano Forte Accompaniment by William Dressler. Large 4to, pp. 7.
New-York: Firth, Pond & Co., 1862

192. FOSTER (STEPHEN C.). Foster's Melodies No. 41. Fairy Belle Song. Written and Composed by Stephen C. Foster. Large 4to, pp. 5.
New York: Firth, Pond & Co., 1859

193. FOSTER (STEPHEN C.). Love and Sentimental Songster. 16mo, original wrappers, pp. 72.     New York [1862]
FINE COPY.

194. FOSTER (STEPHEN C.). Foster's Melodies No. 33. Lulla is Gone. Song written and composed by Stephen C. Foster. Large 4to, pp. 5.
New York: Firth, Pond & Co., 1858
An uncommon title.

195. FOSTER (STEPHEN C.). A Monsier A. F. Dos Santos. Les Bords d'Ohio. And see the rivers how they run, Through woods and meads in Shade and sun. Variations Brillantes sur le theme favori de S. C. Foster. My Old Kentucky Home composees pour le piano par C. H. Grobe. Large 4to, pp. 8.
New York: Firth, Pond & Co., 1853
RARE EDITION. Music only.

196. FOSTER (STEPHEN C.). Old Black Joe. Song and Chorus, written and composed by Stephen C. Foster. *Lithographed cover of Dan Bryant as "Old Black Joe."* Large 4to, pp. 6.     New York: Wm. A. Pond & Co., 1860
Note at top says, "Ten Thousand Copies Sold." SCARCE.

197. [FOSTER (STEPHEN C.).] Old Folks at Home. Words and Music by E. P. Christy. *Fine portrait of Mlle. Nilsson lithographed on front cover.* Large 4to, pp. 5.     Boston: Oliver Ditson & Co., 1870
Christy paid Foster $500.00 to write this song and to allow Christy to claim the authorship.

198. FOSTER (STEPHEN C.). To the Tremaine Family. Why have my Loved ones gone. Ballad. Words and Music by Stephen C. Foster. Large 4to, pp. 5.
New York: Published by Horace Waters [1861]
Very uncommon title by Foster.

199. FOSTER (STEPHEN C.). Foster's Melodies. Willie We Have Missed You. Written and Composed by Stephen C. Foster. *Fine lithograph of Willie being welcomed home, on title.* Large 4to, pp. 5.
New York: Firth, Pond & Co., 1854

200. [FREMONT (GENERAL).] Songs for Freemen: A Collection of Campaign and Patriotic Songs for the People. Adapted to familiar and popular melodies, and designed to promote the cause of "Free Speech, Free Press, Free Soil, Free Men and Fremont." 16mo, original front wrapper with portrait of Fremont, pp. 48.                           Utica: H. H. Hawley, Publisher, 1856
Contains: "Song of the Rocky Mountains;" "All Hail to Fremont," by Elizabeth Whittier; "Pass of the Sierre," etc. Well worn, crudely and close trimmed copy, showing the hard use it was put to in Fremont's exciting campaign for President. Not in Harris collection of Songsters.

201. [GREELEY (HORACE).] "The Farmer of Chappaqua" Songster. Containing a Great Number of the Best Campaign Songs that the Unanimous and Enthusiastic Nomination of The Hon. Horace Greeley, for President has produced. . . . *Embellished with a Splendid Steel Engraving of the Hon. Horace Greeley executed by the celebrated Artist T. C. Buttree. From a fine picture taken in 1854.* 16mo, original colored wrapper, with portrait, pp. 76 and 20.
New York, 1872
SCARCE, not in Henschel's list of Greeleyana.

202. HARDY (DANIEL, JUN.). A Thanksgiving Anthem. Oblong 16mo, original wrappers, pp. 32.
Boston: Printed by Manning & Loring for the Author, Nov. 1808
PRIVATELY PRINTED. Words and music by an early American composer of whom little is known. Not in Harris Songster collection, Sturges, etc.

203. HAWTHORNE (ALICE—Pseudonym of Sep. Winner). Yes! I would the War Were Over. Sung by Sig. R. Abecco. Words by Alice Hawthorne. Music by George T. Evans. Large 4to, pp. 5
Published by M. Gray, No. 613 Clay Street, San Francisco [Cal.] 1863
RARE CALIFORNIA MUSIC SHEET. This Song was written as a companion to the popular song, "When this Cruel War is Over." "Alice Hawthorne" was a pseudonym used by Sep. Winner.

204. HAYS (WILL). Poems and Songs. *Portrait.* 8vo, cloth, pp. [7], 6 to 124.
Louisville, Ky., Chas. T. Dearing, 1895
The author was the well-known ballad writer. Not in Sturges, McKee or Maier.

205. HARRISON MEDAL MINSTREL; comprising a collection of the most Popular and Patriotic Songs, illustrative of the enthusiastic feelings of a grateful but power ridden people towards the gallant defender of their country. The Hero—the Patriot—The Farmer—the Statesman—and Philanthropist. . . 32mo, original wrappers, pp. 192.       Philadelphia, Grigg & Elliott, 1840
SCARCE POLITICAL SONG—Harrison of Tippecanoe fame.

206. HARRISON MELODIES, Original and Selected. Published under the direction of the Boston Harrison Club. 18mo, original wrappers, pp. 72.
Boston: Weeks, Jordan and Company, 1840
Portrait of Harrison on front wrapper. Political Songsters are becoming SCARCE AND VALUABLE.

207. HERBERT (SIDNEY). The Young Volunteer Campaign Methodist designed for the use of Bands of Hope and all other Juvenile Reform Associations. *Woodcuts.* 18mo, original wrappers, pp. 48.
Boston: James M. Usher, Office of the Nation, 1864
Anti-Tobacco, Liquor, and Profanity Songster.

33

208. HIMES (JOSHUA V.) AND LITCH (JOSIAH). Millennial Musing: A Choice Selection of Hymns, designed for the use of Second Advent Meetings. 32mo, original printed boards, pp. 144.

Boston: Published 14 Devonshire St., 1841

THE FIRST COLLECTION OF "SECOND ADVENT" HYMNS PRINTED. Not listed among the Harris collection of Songsters.

209. HOWE (ELIAS, JR.). The Ethiopian Glee Book: containing the Songs sung by the Christy Minstrels, with many other Popular Negroe Melodies, in four parts, arranged for Quartett Clubs. By Gumbo Chaff, A. M. A. First Banjo Player to the King of Congo. Oblong 12mo, original printed wrappers, pp. [2], 59 to 111 and [1]. Boston: Published by Elias Howe . . . 1848

No. 2 of the Ethiopian Glee Book, published by the author.

## RARE DETROIT "ORATORIO" ON THE PILGRIMS

210. HOWE (U. TRACY). The Pilgrims of 1620. An Oratorio. The words by U. Tracy Howe. The Music composed and respectfully dedicated to the New-England Society of Detroit, by Charles Hess. 8vo, original printed wrappers, pp. 11.

Detroit: Published by C. Morse and Son. (G. W. Pattison Commercial Bulletin Printing House] 1849

EXTREMELY RARE. The first Oratorio with a historical theme for its motive as presented in the West. Ritter in his *History of Music in America* gives no account of an Oratorio being presented in any part of the West.

211. [JUDSON (E. E.).]. The Waving Plume, Song Written and dedicated to his Friends and former Comrades. The Officers of the 8th Regt. U. S. Infantry. Gen. Worth's Old Regiment by Ned Buntline. Music by I. B. Woodbury. Large 4to, pp. 5. Boston: Published by Martin & Beals . . . 1847

Rare Song poem by that famous writer of "Beadle" Indian Stories. Gen. Worth was known by the soubriquet of "The Waving Plume," therefore the choice of above title.

212. KENNEDY (JOHN). The American Songster, containing a Choice Selection of about One Hundred and Fifty Modern and Popular Songs as sung by Mr. Sloman, Pearman, Jefferson, Barnes, Cowell, Phillips [and names of 24 more American Actors]. Including Mr. Sloman's Analyzation; or What are Mortals made of. 32mo, old calf, pp. 256.

Baltimore: Published by John Kennedy, 1836

Published by the author. Not in the Harris collection of Songsters. Contains: "Battle of North Point;" "Battle of Plattsburg;" "Battle of New Orleans;" "Boys of Ohio;" "Erie and Champlain;" "Hurrah for the Red, White, and Blue;" "Hunters of Kentucky;" "New Jackson Song;" "Song— Sinclair's Defeat" [in the Western Territory, 1791]; "Star Spangled Banner;" "You Parliament of England" [a song of the Naval Battles, War of 1812]; etc.

## THE EARLIEST AMERICAN MUSICAL WORK WITH A TUNE
## TITLED "CALIFORNIA"

213. KIMBALL (JACOB, JR.). The Rural Harmony, being an Original Composition, In Three and Four Parts. For the Use of Singing Schools and Musical Societies. [5 lines verse from Shakespeare.] Oblong 18mo, original boards, pp. 112.

Published according to Act of Congress. Printed, Typographically, at Bos-

[*Continued*

ton, By Isaiah Thomas and Ebenezer T. Andrews . . . 1793

On page 21 is a tune entitled, "CALIFORNIA," the EARLIEST PRINTED in an American Tune Book. Not in Harris Songster collection, etc.

214. LOG CABIN MINSTREL: or Tippecanoe Songster: containing A Selection of Songs, original and selected, many of them written expressly for this work. Compiled, published and arranged by a member of the Roxbury Democratic Whig Association, and respectfully dedicated to the Log Cabin Boys of the United States. 12mo, original printed wrappers, pp. 60.

Roxbury: Published at the Patriot and Democrat Office, 1840

Scarce and interesting "Harrison for President" political Songster—Anti-Van Buren and J. C. Calhoun.

215. LINCOLN (ABRAHAM). BRADBURY (WILLIAM B.). To the President of the United States. "Hold on Abraham," Song and Chorus, being a response of Uncle Sam's Boys to the call for "Three Hundred Thousand More" ("Uncle Sam's Boys are coming right along"). Sung with immense success by Wood's Minstrels. . . Large 4to, pp. 5.        New York: Wm. A. Pond & Co., 1862

RARE. Response to "Three Hundred Thousand More."

216. LINCOLN (ABRAHAM). THE NATION IN TEARS! A Dirge, in Memory of the Nation's Chief, Abraham Lincoln. Words by R. C. Music by Konrad Treuer. Large 4to, pp. 4.        [New York: W. Jennings Demorest, 1865]

AN UNUSUAL ITEM. With frontispiece tombstone inscribed, "In Memory of Abraham Lincoln. President of the United States of America. Born February 12, 1809. Died April 15th, 1865." "With malice toward none, with charity for all," etc. The words and music on both pages are printed within a heavy black border.

217. LINCOLN (ABRAHAM). CLARK (JAMES G.). The Martyr of Liberty in memory of President Lincoln. Poetry and Music by James G. Clark. Author of "Voice of the Army," "Let me die with my face to the Foe," "Moonlight and Starlight," "Beautiful Annie." Large 4to, pp. 6.

New York: Horace Waters . . . 1865

Not in Sturges, etc.

218. LINCOLN (ABRAHAM). CODY (HON. H. H.). The Death Knell is Tolling. Quartette. A Requiem to the memory of our late beloved President Abraham Lincoln. Written by Hon. H. H. Cody. Music by J. F. Fargo. *Title printed within heavy checkered border.* Large 4to, pp. 5.

Chicago, Lyon & Healy, 1865

Rare Chicago memento of Lincoln.

219. LINCOLN (ABRAHAM). COOPER (GEORGE). Our Noble Chief has passed away. Elegy on the death of Abraham Lincoln. Music by J. R. Thomas. Large 4to, pp. 5.        New York: Wm. A. Pond & Co. . . . 1865

220. LINCOLN (ABRAHAM). DUDLEY (JAMES T.). Our Flag, Our Army and Our President Quartette. Words by James T. Dudley. Music by William H. Perry. Large 4to, pp. 5.        New York: Horace Waters . . . 1864

221. LINCOLN (ABRAHAM). LADD (M. B.). To the Memory of Abraham Lincoln. Who died a martyr to the cause of Freedom. Lincoln's Dying Refrain. [5 lines verse.] Large 4to, pp. 5.        Philadelphia: W. R. Smith . . . 1865

222. LINCOLN (ABRAHAM). HAWTHORNE (ALICE—Pseudonym of Sep. Winner). In Memory of Abraham Lincoln, Sixteenth President of the United States. A Nation Mourns Her Martyr'd Son ("An Honest Man's the Noblest Work of God"). Words by Alice Hawthorne, music by Sep. Winner. Large 4to, pp. 6.                                   Philadelphia: Sep. Winner, 1865
"Alice Hawthorne" was a pseudonym used by Sep. Winner.

223. LINCOLN (ABRAHAM). TURNER (J. W.). A Nation Weeps. Dirge on the Death of Abraham Lincoln, By J. W. Turner. *Title printed within dark heavy fancy borders.* Large 4to, pp. 5.                          Boston: Oliver Ditson & Co., 1865
Not in Sturges, etc.

224. LINCOLN (JAIRUS). Anti-Slavery Melodies: for the Friends of Freedom. Prepared for the Hingham Anti-Slavery Society. 8vo, original printed wrappers, worn, pp. 96.      Hingham (Mass.): Published by Elijah B. Gill [1843]
SCARCE. A copy well-worn from use in the Anti-Slavery Cause. Not in McKee or Maier.

225. MACARTHY (HARRY). To Albert G. Pike, Esq. The Poet Lawyer of Arkansas. The Bonnie Blue Flag. Composed, Arranged and Sung at his Personation Concerts By Harry Macarthy. The Arkansas Comedian. *Music Sheet, cover in colors.* 4to, 6 pp.
        New Orleans: Published by A. E. Blackman & Bros . . . 1861
RARE AND INTERESTING Southern Music Sheet.

226. MACKLIN (CHARLES). Love A-La Mode: A Comedy in two acts. As performed at the Theatres Drury-Lane, Convent-Garden and New York. 18mo, sewed, pp. 38 and [2].                              New York: D. Longworth, 1811
The last unnumbered leaf reads: "The following Song was introduced and sung in Love A-la-mode by Mrs. Oldmixon in the New-York Theatre, viz.: "The Ladies Cuckoo"—I. "For the rights of the fair
        Here I stand I declare
        Unless there's an advocate here,
        Not a man do I see
        Will the task take from me," etc.
The above is the earliest song sung on the American stage advocating "Equal Rights" and "Franchises" for Women in America.

227. MAGAZINE OF WIT, and American Harmonist, containing a collection of the most admired anecdotes, and a variety of the best Songs, chiefly composed in Honour of the Naval and Military Victories gained during The Late War. *Embellished with a Representation of Perry's Victory.* 18mo, boards, leather back.                            Philadelphia: McCarthy & Davis . . . 1821
RARE WAR OF 1812 SONGSTER. Not in Harris Songster collection, etc. Songs: "Perry's Victory;" "Trumpet of Fame" [Constitution and Guerriere Song]; "Banks of Champlain;" "Star Spangled Banner;" "Mason's Farwell;" "Bucket," by Woodworth; "Lawrence the Brave;" "Siege of Plattsburg;" "Immortal Washington;" "American Commerce and Freedom;" "Lawrence's Victory;" "Tars of Columbia;" "Columbia's Hardy Seamen;" etc.

228. MORRIS (GEORGE P.). My Hoosier Girl. Song & Chorus. Sung by the Barker Family, written by Geo. P. Morris, Esq. Music composed by Nathan Barker. . . . Large 4to, pp. 5.          Indianapolis: A. E. Jones & Co., 1854
Rare Indiana Song by Geo. P. Morris the noted Poet and Ballad writer. FIRST EDITION.

229. NATIONAL CLAY MINSTREL (The): and True Whig's Pocket Companion, for the Presidential Canvass of 1844. *Frontispiece and woodcut illustration.* 18mo, cloth, pp. 126.                    Philadelphia: George Hood [1843]

"Harry of the West" for President Songster.

230. NATIONAL CLAY MINSTREL and True Whig's Pocket Companion for the Presidential Canvass of 1844. 18mo, original printed wrappers, pp. 126.
Boston: James Fisher [1844]

VERY SCARCE. By George Hood.
New and improved edition with the following new songs: "Days when we went canvassing, Harry Clay raisin;" "The Voice of the People;" "Farewell Speech of Henry Clay to the United States Senate." This work should have been called "Clay's Kentucky Songster," as it is very strong on the Kentucky end.

231. NATIONAL CLAY MELODIST. A collection of Popular and Patriotic Songs. Second edition, enlarged and improved. *Portrait of Clay and many interesting woodcuts.* 18mo, original printed wrappers, pp. 108.
Boston: Benj. Adams, 1844

By John H. W. Warland. Contains new songs, as follows: "Bonny Clay Flag;" "The Kentuckian Broom Girl;" "The Grand Backing Out;" "Rousing Song;" etc., etc. VERY SCARCE.

232. NEW BOOK (THE) of Temperance Melodies. *Woodcuts.* 32mo, original printed wrappers, pp. [95] unnumbered.
Philadelphia, New York, Boston and Baltimore: Fisher & Brothers [185–]

With a few "scare-em-to-death" woodcuts. Not in Harris Songster collection.

233. NIGHTINGALE (THE), or, Musical Companion, being a collection of Entertaining Songs. *Woodcut of nightingale on title.* 18mo, original boards, pp. 72.
New York: Printed and sold by Smith & Forman, at the Franklin Juvenile Bookstores, 195 and 213 Greenwich Street, 1814

Songs: "On the Death of Franklin;" "America, Commerce and Freedom;" "An Ode, Composed for the Typographical Society," by a Member; Other songs are Sea Song, Irish, Kissing and other subjects. Not in Harris Songster collection, etc.

234. OLMSTEAD (T.). The Musical Olio Containing I. A concise introduction to the Art of singing by note. II. A Variety of Psalm Tunes, Hymnes and Set-Pieces. . . . Oblong 18mo, original sheep, pp. 10, 3, 10 to 112.
Published according to Act of Congress. Printed Typographically at Northampton. By Andrew Wright. 1805

At end are 6 pages of manuscript Music, very finely executed, including one entitled, "New York." Not in Harris, etc.

235. [ORIGINAL HYMNS AND POEMS.] Celebration of West India Emancipation, by the Hingham and Weymouth Anti-Slavery Societies, in Hingham, August 1, 1842. 8vo, sewed, pp. 12.                         [Hingham] 1842

Hymns and poems by M. L. Gardner, Wm. L. Garrison, John Pierpont, etc. Not in Sturges, Harris, McKee or Maier.

236. PERCIVAL (JAMES G.). Dirge [Words by Jas. G. Percival] Sung at the Consecration of the Soldiers' Cemetery at Gettysburg [Nov. 19th, 1863]; Composed and arranged for Four Voices by Alfred Delaney. Large 4to, pp. 5.
Philadelphia: Lee & Walker [1863]

RARE ITEM BY PERCIVAL THE POET. Dedicated to Andrew G. Curtin, Governor of Pennsylvania. Not in Sturges, etc.

237. PILGRIM'S LEGACY (THE). "A Church without a Bishop," "A State without a King." As Sung at the Broadway Tabernacle Feby. 26th, 1844. Large 4to, pp. 3.                    New York: Mark H. Newman . . . 1844

With fine lithographic view of the "Landing of the Pilgrims" in 1620.

238. POST-CHAISE COMPANION (THE); or, Magazine of Wit. By Carlo Convivio Socio, Junr. Fellow of the Royal Academy of Humourists. To which is added, A Number of Patriotic and Humorous Songs. Second Edition. 16mo, boards, pp. 142, uncut edges.                    Philadelphia, 1821

PRIVATELY PRINTED. Not in Sturges, Harris, McKee, Maier, etc.
Contains "Saint-Helena. A Poem: By a Yankee" (i. e.) John Kearsley Mitchell. 26 pp.; "The Lawyer: A tale (in verse) showing how a Lawyer once got to Heaven;" "The Mason's Farewell," poem; "Laurence the Brave"; "A Parlour-Window Book, for Dull Times," (Magazine) Vol. I, January 22, 1821. No. 2. devoted to Mr. Kean the noted actor.
A VERY RARE ITEM.

239. ROOT (GEORGE F.). The Bugle Call. Edited by Geo. F. Root. Oblong 12mo, pp. [2], 60 and [1].                    Cincinnati: John Church & Co. [1863]

A fine copy of a scarce Rebellion Songster, Longfellow's poem, "The Ship of State," is here printed with words and music and is entitled, "The Ship of Union." Other songs are: "Call 'Em Names Jeff;" "Stand by the President" (Lincoln); "A New Ballad of Lord Lovell," the brave defender of New Orleans; "Jefferson D——, Sir;" "English Neutrality;" "Uncle Sam's Funeral;" etc., etc. Not in Harris Songster collection, Sturges, etc.

240. ROUGH AND READY SONGSTER (THE): *Embellished with twenty-five splendid engravings, illustrative of the American Victories in Mexico.* By An American Officer. 32mo, original calf binding, pp. 250 and VI.
                    New-York: Nafis & Cornish, Publishers . . . [1848?]

THE BEST TEXAS-MEXICAN WAR SONGSTER PRINTED.
Contains: "Song of the Texan Ranger;" "Oregon and Texas;" "Texian General's Address to his Army;" "All for Texas;" "Remember the Alamo;" "The Flag of Texas;" "Uncle Sam's Song to Miss Texas;" "Song of Texas;" "Fair Land of Texas;" etc. This volume is simply packed with stirring and appealing songs of the above character.
Not in Sturges, Maier, McKee, etc.

241. RUSSELL (SOL SMITH). Sol Smith Russell's Character Vocalist containing the Character Songs of the inimitable American Humorist and Protean Character Delineator. 16mo, original wrappers, pp. 72.
                    New York [1863]

By the author of *Theatrical Management in the West and South for Thirty Years,* New York, 1868.

242. [SEARSON (JOHN).] Elegiac Verses, on the decease of His Late Excellency, the illustrious and ever-memorable, great and good General George Washington of Immortal Memory. 8vo, unbound, pp. 4. Caption title as issued.
                    [Philadelphia, 1800]

Sometimes bound with the author's poem, *Mount Vernon* printed in Philadelphia [1799]. The New York Public Library lists a copy of above item, it seems to be missing in the Harris collection and was lacking in Sturges and McKee collections.
The author says the above verses can be sung to any long-meter tune or to the 100th Psalm, new.

## A RARE WORK BY OLIVER SHAW, THE NOTED RHODE ISLAND COMPOSER

243. SHAW (OLIVER). The Providence Selection of Psalm and Hymn Tunes. In Two Parts. Part First, containing the rudiments of Musick, and a selection of tunes suitable for all the various measures in use in worshipping assemblies. Part Second, consisting of select pieces, of various measures, for occasional use. Chiefly Selected from the most eminent European Authors and designed for the use of Schools and Churches. 8vo, original boards, pp. 127, [1].

Dedham: Printed by H. Mann and Co. for the Author, 1815

Shaw, although blind, became the most noted Psalm Composer of his period. He was also a Ballad writer, Singer, and Singing-Teacher at the same time. EXTREMELY RARE AND A FINE COPY. The title is printed within heavy ornamental borders and is a neat specimen of printing.

244. SHAW (OLIVER). The Social and Sacred Melodist, consisting of Songs, Duetts, Anthems, &c. Composed and arranged with an accompaniment for the Piano Forte or Organ, and respectfully inscribed to the Lovers of Sacred Harmony. 4to, original boards, pp. 100.

Providence: Published and Sold by the Author, No. 70 Westminister Street, 1835

Not in Dennison's *Shaw Memorial Check List*, which lists the Boston Edition only, this is the RARE AUTHOR'S EDITION.

245. SLOCUM (E. N.). On the Beach at Cape May! Words by E. N. Slocum, As Sung by Lew Simmons, of Carncross & Dixey's Minstrels. Large quarto, pp. 5. [1]. Philadelphia: R. Wittig & Co., No. 1021 Chestnut Street, 1868

A Memento of Cape May, New Jersey, the fashionable summer resort in 1868.

246. SOLDIERS' AND SAILORS' PATRIOTIC SONGS. New York, May, 1864. 8vo, printed wrappers, pp. 19 and [5].

New York: Published by the Loyal Publication Society, 1864

Songs by Holmes, Aldrich, Alfred B. Street, Julia Ward Howe, Bryant, Percival, Bayard Taylor, Charles G. Leland, R. H. Stoddard, George H. Boker, etc., etc. Not in Sturges.

247. SOMMERVILLE (WILLIAM). The Exclusive Claims of David's Psalms. 16mo, original cloth, pp. 189 and errata slip.

Saint John, N. B. Printed by Barnes & Company, Prince William Street 1855

Not verse but a work of reference. Contains chapters in Modern Hymns. A VERY SCARCE CANADIAN WORK.

248. SONGS, DUETS AND CHORUSSES, in the Brilliant Burletta Extravaganza "Fortunio, and his Seven Gifted Servants!" as performed at the Boston Museum. 8vo, original printed wrappers, pp. 8.     [Boston, 183–]

Not in Harris collection of Songsters.

249. SONS OF TEMPERANCE MINSTREL. 32mo, original printed wrappers, pp. 34.

Philadelphia: Joseph Torr [185–]

FINE COPY of an uncommon Temperance Songster. Not in the Harris Songster collection. Written for the Philadelphia "Souses."

250. **SONGSTER'S MUSEUM (THE).** A New and Choice Collection of Popular Songs, selected from the Best Authors. 16mo, boards, pp. 72.

Hartford: Henry Benton, 1835

Songs: "American Volunteer;" "Columbia Land of Liberty;" "Ode Sung at the dinner, given at Boston to the Officers of the United States Frigate *Constitution*, after the victory over the British Frigate *Guerriere;*" "Perry's Victory;" "Sam Jones" (he sail'd along the Jersey Shore, and fish'd for clams); "American Star;" "Battle of the Keys;" "Gunpowder Tea;" "For the Fourth of July;" etc. Not in Harris collection, etc.

251. **SPENCER (J.) AND ROLLINS (E. B.).** New Songs for the Use of Christians. Selected by . . . . 32mo, wrappers, pp. 72.

Woodstock (Vermont), David Watson, 1822

Not noted in Gilman's *Vermont Bibliography.*

252. **SPRINGER (M., JUN'R).** Songs of Zion being a Collection of Hymns for the use of the Pious of all denominations. Fifth edition. 32mo, old calf, pp. 192.

Hallowell (Maine): Printed and Sold by Glazier & Co., sold also by M. Springer, Jun'r, Gardiner . . . 1827

A popular volume of a Maine Hymn Book well used at the period. NOT IN GRIFFITH, etc. Not listed in the Harris collection of Songsters.

253. **STONE (HORATIO).** Eleutheria. A Hymn to Liberty. "All Souls inherit equal rights from Heaven." Music by George Henry Curtis. In vocal score with an accompaniment for the Piano. 4to, pp. [2] and 140.

New York: Wm. Hall & Son . . . 1851

Laid in, are 11 sheets of AUTHOR'S MANUSCRIPTS relating to recital, etc., of this Hymn. Contains 2 pages of subscribers' names. RARE.

254. **THOMPSON'S BAND OF HOPE MELODIES,** consisting of Temperance Songs, Duets, and Glees, especially adapted for Bands of Hope and other Juvenile Temperance Associations. Compiled by Edwin Thompson. 16mo, original wrappers, pp. 72.

Boston, 1864

255. **UNION SONG BOOK (THE);** or, American Sky Lark; From the Most approved modern Songs, A Great Variety of which have never before been printed in America. Containing:

| | |
|---|---|
| Sentimental, | Theatrical |
| Humorous, | Hunting |
| Witty, | Sea and |
| Satyrical. | Masonic Songs |

Also A Number of Toasts and Sentiments. 18mo, old calf, pp. XII, [1], 2 to 312.

Printed at Boston, For William Tileston Clap, No. 88, Fish Street. 1805. David Carlisle, Printer, Cambridge Street

Contains also American Patriotic Songs. THE MASONIC SONGS HAVE A SEPARATE SECTION AT END. Not in the Harris Songster collection. Not in McKee, Maier, Sturges or New York Public Library.

256. **UNIVERSAL COMIC SONGSTER:** being the most Complete ever published, containing all the Songs of Barnes, Jefferson, Dibdin, Coleman, G. Dixon, Sloman, and other eminent vocalists: and many others of eminence, never before published in this country. To which is added a copious list of Toasts, &c. 32mo, original printed boards, pp. 140, [2], stained.

New York: John Lomax, Publisher, 1831

*[Continued*

Contains: "The Yankee Militia Muster;" "The Boston Post Office;" "Fashions of New York;" "Life of an Actor;" "If in New York you would Live;" "Oh, what a town the Bostonians have to talk about;" etc. Not in Harris Songster collection, etc.

257. VOCAL COMPANION; being a selection of Fashionable Songs from the Best Authors. 18mo, original printed wrappers, pp. 72.

Philadelphia: J. W. Smith, 1829

Contains among other songs, "The Hunters of Kentucky;" "America Commerce and Freedom;" "Star Spangled Banner;" "Star of Freedom;" etc., etc.

258. WHIG SONGS for 1844. 8vo, sewed, pp. 15.

[New York: Greeley & McElrath, 1844]

On the last (15th) page is Whittier's poem, "Star of the West." "Henry Clay for President" Songster. Not in Harris, etc.

259. WHITE'S New Ethiopian Song Book containing a collection of all the new and most popular Songs, Glees, Chorusses, Parodies, Duetts, Trios, Burlesques, Lectures, Jokes, Conundrums, &c., as sung by White's Band of Serenaders, Christy's, New Orleans, &c. *Illustrated with numerous engravings.* 18mo, original printed wrappers, pp. 84. New York: H. Long & Brother, 1850

Nice copy of a scarce and interesting Negro Songster.

260. [WITCHEL AND ECKERTSHAUSEN]. Gott ist die reinste Liebe, oder Morgen- und Abend-Opser, in Gebeten, Betrachtungen und Gesangen . . . 12mo, old calf, one clasp, pp. 300.

Reading: Gedruckt by Carl M. Bruckman für Carl McWilliams und Comp.
1822

First 183 pages are verse. Not in Harris. A SCARCE PENNSYLVANIA HYMN BOOK.

261. WOOD ROBIN (THE): A Collection of Songs from the most admired authors. *Frontispiece.* 24mo, original boards, leather back, pp. 192.

Philadelphia: McCarthy & Davis, 1822

Contains some patriotic songs. Not in Harris.

## FOUR UNKNOWN "EPHRATA" SONGSTERS

262. ZUM 8TEN AUGUST 1766. [A Choral with parts as follows: Lit., Gemeine, Chorus, Solo.] 12mo, pp. [4]

[Ephrata, Lancaster Co. Pennsylvania, Bruderschaft] 1766

The note following also applies to the next 3 items listed.

NO OTHER COPY LOCATED IN SEIDENSTICKER, EVANS, HILDEBURN, STURGES OR ELSEWHERE. As the "Ephrata Brotherhood" did its own printing, with a few exceptions, from 1745 to 1786 we take it for granted that the above mentioned imprint is correct, they were not likely to send out to have a small leaflet done elsewhere, besides the fact, that those done outside bore the Printer's name, which would exclude them.

263. ZUM 8TEN AUG. 1768—Gemeine [5 lines then], Aria.
"Laszt uns Ihm nun Hallelujah singen:
Mächtiglich sind wir errett't,
Laszt uns Ihm ein Freudenopfer bringen,
Hier an dieser Friedenstätt" etc. etc.

12mo, pp. [4].

[Ephrata, Lancaster Co., Pennsylvania, Bruderschaft] 1768

NOT IN STURGES OR ANY OTHER KNOWN COLLECTION.

264. ZUM 12ᵀᴱᴺ MAY 1769. In Barby [beginning], Chorus Siehe, wie fein und lieblich ists das Brüder einträchtig bei einander Wohnen . . . Gemeine.
"Der Grund, drauf wir uns gründen,
Ist Christus und Sein Blut,
Das Machet, das wir finden,
Das ew'ge wahre Gut" etc. etc.
12mo. pp. [4].
[Ephrata, Lancaster Co., Pennsylvania, Bruderschaft] 1769
NOT IN STURGES OR ANY OTHER KNOWN COLLECTION.

265. ZUM GEMEIN-FEST IN Bethlehem, den 25sten Jun. 1783.—
Solo
Wohl des Herrn, ermunter dich!
Wer kann deiner Freude wehren?
Sing und Spiele feierlich
Deinem Könige zu Ehren!
Sing Ihm, Er ist wahrlich da:
Ave und Hallelujah!" etc. etc.
12mo, pp. [7].
[Ephrata, Lancaster Co. Pennsylvania, Bruderschaft] 1783
Celebrating a Religious Festival at Bethlehem, Pennsylvania.
NOT IN STURGES OR ANY OTHER KNOWN COLLECTION.

## AMERICAN POETRY — BOOKS AND PAMPHLETS

266. ABANDONED (THE): A Sketch of Life as it may be found in New England. 16mo, original printed wrappers, pp. 32. Boston: Redding and Co, 1848
Poem on a fallen woman. Not in Sturges, McKee nor Maier.

267. ABBEY (HENRY). Ballads of Good Deeds, and Other Verses. Small 8vo, original cloth, pp. 129. New York: D. Appleton & Company, 1872
FIRST EDITION. Not in Sturges or McKee. With bookplate of Melville E. Stone.

268. ABBEY (HENRY). The City of Success and Other Poems. 8vo. cloth, pp. 142 and [2]. New-York: D. Appleton and Company, 1884
FIRST EDITION, actually printed in 1883 although dated 1884. Not in Sturges, McKee or Harris.

269. ABBEY (HENRY). Stories in Verse. 8vo, original gilt cloth, gilt edges, pp. [7], 2 to 128. New York: A. D. F. Randolph & Co. Publishers, 1869
FIRST EDITION. SCARCE. Not in Sturges or McKee.

270. ADAMS (JOHN TURRILL). Poems. 12mo, unbound, pp. 47.
[New Haven:] T. G. Woodward & Co. Printers [1825]
RARE PRIVATELY PRINTED WORK. Not in Sturges, McKee, Maier, etc.

271. AIKEN (JAMES R.—of South Carolina). Gems of Prose and Poetry. The Fruits of Leisure Hours. Original and Selected . . . 8vo. cloth, pp. 225, [2], gilt edges. New York: James Miller. Winslow, S. C. 1876
Not in Sturges. McKee or Maier.

42

272. ALBEE (JOHN). St. Aspenquid of Mt. Agamenticus. An Indian Idyl. 16mo, original wrappers, pp. 24, UNOPENED COPY.

Portsmouth: Published by Lewis W. Brewster, 1879

VERY SCARCE. Not in Sturges, McKee, Harris, Maier, etc.

273. ALFORD (REV. L. A.). Masonic Gem: consisting of Odes, Poem and Dirge. By Rev. L. A. Alford, Logansport, Ind. Being a miniature Sketch of Esoteric and Exoteric Masonry. Second Edition. 12mo, original cloth, pp. 48.

New York: Masonic Publishing and Manufacturing Company, 432 Broome Street, 1868

SCARCE AND FINE COPY by this Indiana Poet. Not in Sturges, McKee, Harris or Maier.

274. ALLEN (B., JR.). Urania, or The True Use of Poesy; A Poem. 18mo, new cloth, pp. 192. UNCUT EDGES.

New-York: Published by A. H. Inskeep, and Bradford, & Inskeep, Phila- delphia. 1814

Not in Sturges, McKee or Maier. Among the other poems are: "Lines Written at New Haven, Conn," "Ode to the Manhattan School;" etc.

275. ALLEN (MISS CHARLOTTE). Poems. 16mo, original cloth, pp. VIII, [1], 2 to 143. Boston: Published by Saxon & Pierce . . . 1841

FIRST EDITION. Not in Sturges, McKee, Maier or Harris (who had the second edition of 1843 only).
Includes: Poem, "Reflections on the Disaster of the Lexington, January 13, 1840" (burned in Long Island Sound).

276. [ALSOP (RICHARD).] The Enchanted Lake of the Fairy Morgana . . . From the Orlando Inamorato of Francesco Berni. 8vo, original boards, pp. VII, [2], 2 to 67.

New York: Printed and Published by Isaac Riley and Co. Lexitypographic Office. 1806

The above is by "One of the Hartford Wits." RARE, not in Sturges, Harris, McKee, Maier or New York Public Library.

277. AMERICAN POETICAL MISCELLANY (THE). Original and Selected. [2 lines verse.] 12mo, old calf (one cover loose), pp. 304.

Philadelphia: Robert Johnson,—1809

Contains: "An Ode" commemorative of the deaths of Lieutenant Somers of the American Navy, and his brave Companions before Tripoli, in the Summer of 1805, "Freedom of Peace, or The Voice of America," won the Prize Medal offered by the Philadelphia Military Association (by Mr. Wilson); Poem, "On the Grave of Baron De Kalb;" and others by Charles H. Wharton, Timothy Dwight, etc. Not in Sturges, Harris, McKee or Maier.

278. AMES (NATHAN). Pirates' Glen and Dungeon Rock. 16mo, original cloth, pp. 64, [2]. Boston, Redding & Company, 1853

Historical poem on Saugus [Lynn] Mass., period 1658. Some of the persons repre- sented are Don, a Pirate; Ross, proprietor of the Iron Works at Saugus; Na-Na-Pas- He-Met, and Ya-Wa-Ta, daughter the Indian Chief. Not in Sturges, McKee or Maier.

279. AMES (NATHANIEL). "Victory emplor'd for Success against the French in America" [In] An Astronomical Diary, Or, an Almanack For the Year of our Lord Christ 1747 . . . 16mo, sewed, pp. [16]

Boston in New England: Printed by John Draper, for the Booksellers [1746]

[Continued

Poem on title and under each month of the year and the first mentioned poem taking up all of the last leaf and dated October 18, 1746.
Not in Sturges, McKee, Harris, Maier, etc.

280. AMSBARY (WALLACE BRUCE). The Ballads of Bourbonnais. *With pictures by Will Vawter.* 8vo, cloth, pp. 182.
Indianapolis, Bobbs-Merrill Company [1904]
French-Canadian Poems by Early French-Canadian Settlers in KankakeeCounty, Illinois, with a sketch of their history.

281. ANTEDILUVIAN, or, Serpentine Musings. By a Descendant of Noah. *Illustrations.* 8vo, original cloth, pp. 97.
New York: Published for the Author by G. P. Putnam's Sons, 1874
Not in Sturges, McKee, Harris or Maier. We quote a few lines:
"So Satin being long and slim,
Stretched up and bent her down a limb."
"Adam and Eve the World begun,
Adam he carded, and Eve she spun"
(inscribed on the Devil's tail at end)

282. ARTHUR (T. S.—Editor). The Sons of Temperance Offering: for 1850. *Plates.* Original full red roan, gilt, gilt edges., 8vo, pp. 320.
New York: Nafish & Cornish [1850]
Although worn, this is still a good example of early American gilt decorated red roan binding. Arthur was the author of "Ten Nights in a Bar Room," famous for a long term of years—now forgotten. Not in Sturges, Harris, McKee or Maier.

283. [ASHMEAD (CATHARINE FORRESTER).] Fallings from A Lady's Pen. 8vo, original cloth, pp. 85. Philadelphia: Lindsay and Blakiston, 1849
Dedicated to Nat P. Willis. Contains poems: "To Halleck;" "The Disinterment of Napoleon;" "South Carolina;" "On Flirting;" "Poem to Shelley;" etc. Not in Sturges, McKee, Harris or Maier.

284. ASSEE (CHS. ERYL SECUNDYNE). Laus Reginae, A Memorial Tribute [in verse]. 12mo, original printed boards, pp. 100 and Epilogue leaf.
Trinidad: Franklin's Electric Printery, 12, Abercromby Street, Port-of-Spain [1902]
PRESENTATION COPY. Inscribed: *Presented to James Carleton Young, Esqre with the author's compliments and best wishes and admiration.* C. S. Assee, 25/6/07. On back of front cover the author has written a poem,—"To James Carleton Young, Esq. (Bibliophile)," 14 lines of verse, signed and dated Port-of-Spain, 25 June, 1907.

285. [BANGS (JOHN KENDRICK).] The Lorgnette, 1886. *Illustrated.* Oblong 12mo, cloth, pp. 32. New York: George J. Coombes, 275 Fifth Ave. [1886]
THIS AUTHOR'S FIRST PUBLICATION. In the Sturges sale, "Roger Camerden" was catalogued as Bangs' first publication. The above book proves otherwise being printed a year earlier.
Not in Sturges, McKee or Harris.

286. BARHITE (JARED). Our Profession and Other Poems. *Portrait.* 12mo, cloth, pp. 232.
Published by William E. Barhite . . . Long Island City, N. Y., 1895
The author was Principal of the Third Ward Grammar School, Long Island City, N. Y. Not in Sturges, McKee or Maier.

287. BARRETT (S. A.). Maintonomah, and Other Poems. 8vo, cloth, pp. 209.
New York: Cody and Burgess . . . MDCCCXLIX (1849)
Poem on the Mohawk Indians. Not in Sturges, McKee or Maier.

288. BARRY (GARRETT). Poems on Several Occasions. 16mo, half old morocco, pp. 101 and [15].

Baltimore: Printed for Cole, & I. Bonsal and John Vance & Co. . . . 1807

SCARCE UNCUT COPY. Contains: "Lines occasioned by attending the examination of the students in St. Mary's College, Baltimore;" "On the Death of General Washington;" "To the Young Ladies of Baltimore, occasioned by the frequent illiberal remarks on their mode of dress, which appeared in the different papers of this city."

289. BATTLE OF CANNAE (THE), and Terrible Overthrow of the Roman Army; An Historical Poem and Diagram. . . . *Lithographic plates*. 8vo, original cloth, pp. [5], 2 to 54.

Baltimore: Published for the Author by Joseph Neal, 1856

PRIVATELY PRINTED POEM. The preface deals much with the cremation of the dead, the poem in part deals on the same subject. Not in Sturges, Harris, McKee or Maier.

290. BEARDSLEY (JANE MARGARET MATTHEWS). The Unforgotten and Other Poems. 8vo, original cloth, pp. VII, [2], 2 to 90, [2].

[New Haven] Privately Printed, 1891

ORIGINAL MANUSCRIPT POEM on last 2 fly-leaves. SCARCE. The Authoress was born on St. Simons Island, Georgia, moved to Connecticut in 1848. Most of the scenes of these poems are laid in Cheshire, Connecticut. Not in Sturges, McKee or Maier.

291. BECKETT (SYLVESTER B.). Hester, The Bride of the Islands. A Poem. 8vo, original cloth, pp. 336.     Portland: Bailey & Noyes. MDCCCLX (1860)

A long narrative poem, containing many fine descriptions of Casco Bay, Maine. Not in Sturges, McKee, Harris or Maier.

292. BEERS (ETHEL LYNN). All Quiet Along the Potomac and Other Poems. 8vo, cloth, pp. 352, gilt edges.     Philaelphia: Porter & Coates [1879]

FIRST EDITION. Not in Sturges, McKee or Maier.

293. BEITH (JOHN). Life [Poems, etc.] of John Beith. The Blind Scottish Newsman of New York. By A Brither Scot. *Lithographic portrait of Beith by Joseph Laing, Lith., N. Y.* 8vo, original printed wrappers, pp. 45 and [21 of advertisements].

New York: Published for the Sole Benefit of John Beith, 1880

Not known to Ross in his *Scottish Poets in America*, and lacking in Sturges, McKee, Harris, Maier, etc.

294. [BIGLER (DAVID).] The Orphan Twins; or, The Adventures of A Brother and Sister. A Poem. 12mo, original cloth, pp. 100.

New York: Stanford and Swords, 1849

Written and published to get funds to buy a site for a place of worship for the United Brethren (or Moravians) of Brooklyn, New York. Not in Sturges, McKee or Maier.

295. BIGLOW (WILLIAM). Education: A Poem spoken at Cambridge at the request of the Phi Beta Kappa, July 18th, 1799. 8vo, cloth, pp. 17.

Printed at Salem, by Joshua Cushing, 1799

This poem is for the most part a witty satire, on the educational methods then in vogue. The author attempts "To prove that men were fools in every age." FINE COPY. Autograph of Saml. Thatcher on title.

Not in the Sturges, Harris, McKee or Maier collections. The only copy located is the New York Public Library copy, lacking title-page and first two and the last leaf.

45

296. [BIGLOW (WILLIAM).] Re-Commencemnt, Commencement Again, Commencement in Earnest, Commencement Indeed, &c., called also, Censure, Scandal, Vague Report, Common Fame, Matters and Things in General, or, What You Please. Recited before "The Associated Instructors of Youth in the Town of Boston," October 30, 1811. By a Brother . . . 8vo, sewed, pp. 8, UNCUT EDGES.          Boston. Printed by J. Belcher, 1811

> THIS ORIGINAL FIRST EDITION printed in Boston is lacking in the Sturges, Harris, McKee, Maier, and N. Y. Public Library collections, the Salem, 1812 edition is fairly common.

297. [BIGLOW (WILLIAM).] Re-Re-Commencement; A Kind of a Poem; Calculated to be recited before an "Assemblage" of New England Divines, of all the various Denominations; but which never was so recited, and in all human probability never will be. By a Friend of Every Body and Every Soul . . . 8vo, unbound, pp. 8.
   Salem: Printed by Thomas C. Cushing, 1812

> Author was a graduate of Harvard in 1794 and later was for several years principal of the noted Boston Latin School which he conducted with distinguished success.

298. BINDER (HEINRICH). Liederklange aus vie Jahrzehnten. 8vo, original cloth, pp. 142, [3].
   Zu beziehn durch Gustave E. Stechert, 180 Broadway, New York, 1895

> Poems include: "Westward the Star of Empire Takes its Way;" "Amerikanische Poesie;" Poems relating to New York, Detroit, G. A. R.; "Saint Schabbes, a Bigger Man than Washington;" "Deutscher 'Pork Boycott';" "In Memoriam, John Charles Fremont;" "James Russell Lowell; "John Ericson;" "Sklaven Ruf an Lincoln" etc. A SCARCE VOLUME OF GERMAN-AMERICAN VERSE. Not in Sturges, Maier or McKee. The author was a noted Journalist.

### RARE RHODE ISLAND ORATION IN PROSE AND VERSE

299. BINNEY (BARNABAS). An Oration delivered On the late Public Commencement at Rhode-Island College in Providence, September 1774. Being a Plea for the Right of Private Judgement in Religious Matters; or, For the Liberty of Choosing our own Religion. Corroborated By the well known Consequences of Priestly Power, to which are annexed, The Valedictions of the Class then first Graduated. By Barnabas Binney, A. B. [Quotations in verse from Milton and Rowe.] . . . 4to, marbled wrappers, pp. 44.
   Boston: Printed and Sold by John Kneeland, in Milk Street, MDCCLXXIV
   (1774)

> Poem to the Residents at College, to the President and Professor, to his Class-Mates Messires John Dorrance, Dwight Foster, Timothy Jones, Jacob Mann and Elias Penniman. Small defect in title. Not in Sturges, McKee, Harris, New York Public Library, Maier, etc.

300. BISHOP (PUTNAM P.). Liberty's Ordeal. 12mo, original cloth, pp. 128.
   New York: Sheldon & Company . . . 1864

> Half the poem relates to the doings of the Rebels up to the Fort Sumter affair. Not in Sturges, McKee or Maier.

301. BLADENSBURG RACES (THE). 8vo, original printed wrappers, pp. 8.
   No place, printer, *circa* 186–

> Bitter and disrespectful poem, especially against President Madison, written soon after the Battle, but not printed until 1816—the author's name is unknown.
> A curiosity among the poetical literature brought forth through the War of 1812. This reprint, done about 186–, is not listed in Sturges, Harris, McKee or Maier collections.

302. BLEECKER (ANN ELIZA). The Posthumous Works of Ann Eliza Bleecker, in Prose and Verse. To which is added, A Collection of Essays, Prose and Poetical by Margaretta V. Faugeres. *Fine engraved portrait of Mrs. Bleecker by Tiebout.* 16mo, three-quarter rough-grained morocco, pp. [13], II to XVIII, [1] and 20 to 375.

New York: Printed by T. and J. Swords, No. 27, William-Street, 1793

The first poet and novelist of Tomhanick, N. Y.

Tomhanick, a little village 17 miles above Albany was near the seat of trouble between the "Vermonters" and "Yorkers" over the Boundary Line, the author's husband taking a prominent part therein, of which an account is given in letters included in this volume. Many letters treat on the events of the American Revolution, Arnold's Treason, and events which occurred near the author's home. The "History of Maria Kittle" contained in this volume is an account of Murder and Captivity by and among the Indians during the Revolution. One of the longest poems in this volume, entitled "The Hudson," is written in a historic and patriotic style. The above work was written by Mother and Daughter and is rare. Not in Sturges.

303. BOIES (LURA ANNA). Rural Rhymes and Literary Remains of Lura Anna Boies with her Biography by Mrs. Helen McFradenburgh, Recollections by George W. Bungay and Part of a Sermon by Rev. Professor King. [4 lines verse.] Christmas A. D. 1860. *Engraved portrait.* 8vo, original cloth and glazed wrappers, pp. 302.

Saratoga Springs: Steam Presses of G. M. Davidson, 1860

The original glazed and printed wrappers are bound in. Contains poem, pp. 17 to 34 on "Jane McCrea the Indian Captive" who was killed and horribly mangled by the Indians during the Revolutionary War. Not in Sturges, McKee or Maier.

304. BOURNE (WILLIAM OLAND). Poems of the Republic. A Contribution to the Metropolitan Fair. 12mo, original printed wrappers, pp. 48.

New York, Edward O. Jenkins, No. 20 North William Street, 1864

Not in Sturges, Harris, McKee or Maier.

### EARLIEST AMERICAN LEGAL POEM

305. BRACKETT (J. WARREN). The Ghost of Law, or, Anarchy and Despotism. A Poem, delivered before the Phi Beta Kappa, Dartmouth College, at their Anniversary, August 23, 1803. And this I know, that, where law ends Tyranny begins. Chatham [3 lines of verse from Virgil in Latin]. 4to, unbound, pp. 24. Hanover (N. H.): Printed by Moses Davis, 1803

THE EARLIEST SEPARATELY PRINTED AMERICAN POEM DEVOTED ENTIRELY TO LAW. Not in Sturges, McKee, Maier, New York Public Library lists and NOT KNOWN to Otis in his *History of American Verse 1625–1807.* A full-size copy as issued —the only other copy I can trace (the Harris copy) was cut down to 12mo size according to description.

306. BRADFORD (WILLIAM). A Dialogue or, Third Conference between some young men born in New England, and some ancient men which came out of Holland and Old England concerning the Church and Government Thereof. [With some verses.] Edited with a Preface and Notes by Charles Dean. Reprinted from the Proceedings of the Massachusetts Historical Society. 8vo, original cloth, pp. XII, [3], 2 to 78.

Boston: Press of John Wilson and Son, 1870

The poems are entitled: "Some observations of God's Merciful dealing with us in this wilderness, and his gracious protection over us these many years. Blessed be his Name;" and "New Plymouth." Originally written in 1652 it is now here printed in full for the first time. Nice copy, but Library stamp on title and on some other pages.

Not in Sturges, Harris, McKee, Maier or New York Public Library. This is the PRIVATELY PRINTED AUTHOR'S EDITION, printed one year before the Society *Proceedings* which was issued in 1871.

307. [BROOKS (C. T.) AND OTHERS.] The American Celebration in Paris, Thursday Evening, December 7, 1865 . . . pp. [2], 33. Paris: Printed by E. Briere, 1865; [AND] Celebration of Washington's Birth Day in Rome. February 22nd, 1866 at the Galleria Dantesca. pp. 43. [Rome(?)] 1866. 2 vols. in one, 8vo, vellum, gilt back.          Paris, 1865; [Rome(?)] 1866
> The above 2 pamphlets were specially bound and presented by Mr. John Jay of New York to Mrs. Morgan. BOTH ARE RARE PRIVATELY PRINTED ITEMS. One contains an address by John Hay. C. T. Brooks of Newport, Laura C. Redden of St. Louis, and W. W. Story, the American artist in Rome, wrote poems for the several occasions. Not in Sturges, Harris, McKee or Maier.

308. BROOKS (N. C.). The Amethyst, an Annual of Literature. Edited and Published by N. C. Brooks. *Plates.* 18mo, original silk cloth, gilt edges, pp. 290, frayed at edges, cover loose.
> Baltimore: Printed by William A. Francis. MDCCCXXXI (1831)
> THIS RARE ANNUAL CONTAINS 8 FINE LITHOGRAPHIC PLATES BY ENDICOTT AND SWETT. The Artist in each case was Swett. One is of the "Indian Chief Ontwa." The entire contents in prose and verse are original articles by Baltimorians only, comprising,—"The Wreckers," Prize Poem by J. H. Hewitt; "Lines to the Memory of Edward C. Pinckney," by W. A. M.; etc., etc. Among the prose items are several fine Indian Tales,—"Loweka," by J. N. McJilton, and "The Curse of Tahloosin," by J. H. Hewitt. The lithograph plates are some of the earliest if not the earliest used in an Annual. The first number of this annual issued. Not in Sturges, McKee, Harris or Maier.

309. BROOKS (PHILLIPS). Poems. *Plates in black and colors.* 4to, cloth, pp. [48].
> London: Ernest Nister [1894]
> Printed by E. Nister at Nuremberg, Bavaria, Germany. A nice volume and scarce. Not in Sturgis, McKee or Maier.

310. BROOKS (SARAH WARNER). The Legend of St. Christopher and Other Poems. 8vo, original cloth, pp. V, [5], 3 to 172.
> Providence: George H. Whitney, 1859
> Rhode Island Author. Not in Sturges, McKee or Maier.

## THE RAREST OF CHARLES BROCKDEN BROWN'S WORKS

311. [BROWN (CHARLES BROCKDEN).] The Monthly Magazine, and American Review, for the Year 1799: From April to December inclusive. Vol. I (ALL EVER ISSUED). 8vo, unbound, pp. 4 and 480, UNCUT EDGES.
> New York: Printed and sold by T. & J. Swords, 1800 [1799]
> Only 6 numbers of this rare periodical by Brown were issued as follows,—April, May, June, July, August (single numbers) and September, October, November and December, the last four months issued in one number, 1799.
> Has a few defects, as follows,—contents leaf has small rip, first page of June number imperfect and some leaves of last number stained.
> Among the verse in this volume are the following poems: "Monody on the Death of George Washington, delivered at the New York Theatre, on Monday Evening, December 30, 1799;" "Poem on the Death of Gen. George Washington."
> Lacking in the Sturges, McKee and all other noted collections.

312. BROWN (F. W. A. S.). A Valedictory Poem; addressed to the Inhabitants of Rainsford's, George's, Gallops', Light House, and Deer Islands, in Boston Harbour. Second Edition. 16mo, wrappers, pp. 52.
> Boston: Printed by True & Weston, 1819
> Poems: "Shipwreck near Lowell's Island;" "Battle between the Chesapeake and Shannon;" "Ode to the memory of Capt. J. Laurence;" "Sailing Directions into the [Boston] Harbor," in verse; etc. By a Native of Deer-Island, Boston Harbor. Not in Harris, Maier or New York Public Library List.

313. BROWN (JAMES SCOTT). The Bouquet and Other Poems. 16mo, original cloth, pp. 124.                    Lancaster, Pa., Murray, Young & Co., 1858
  SCARCE VOLUME of Pennsylvania Verse. Not in Sturges, McKee, Harris or Maier collections.


314. BROWN (LELAH HARRISON). A Book of Poems. *Portrait.* 8vo, original cloth, pp. [6], 3 to 70.                    No place, no printer [1892]
  SCARCE PRIVATELY PRINTED VERSE by a St. Louis Author. Dedicated to the soldiers of the late War, North and South. Not in Sturges, McKee, Harris or Maier.


315. BROWNE (FRANCES ELIZABETH). Poems. 12mo, original cloth, pp. IV, [1], 2 to 155.          Cambridge: Metcalf and Company, MDCCCXLVI (1846)
  FIRST EDITION. Poems: "On the Abolition of Slavery in the United States;" "Stanzas Suggested by a View of Boston from the cupola of the State House;" "On Poetry;" etc. Not in Sturges, McKee or Maier.


316. BROWNE (FRANCIS F.—Compiler). Bugle-Echoes. A Collection of Poems of the Civil War, Northern and Southern. *Title printed in red.* 8vo, cloth, pp. 336, gilt edges.
    New-York: White, Stokes, & Allen, MDCCCLXXXVI (1886)
  A volume of really notable Civil War Verse by Albert Pike, Bret Harte, Walt Whitman, Henry Timrod, Bryant, Holmes, Lowell, Read, Taylor, Boker, Whittier, Paul Hayne, Sydney Lanier, and a numerous collection of other famous American Poets. Not in Sturges, Harris, McKee or Maier.


317. BRYANT (JOHN HOWARD). Poems written from Youth to Old Age, 1824–1884. *Portrait.* 8vo, cloth, pp. 239.
    Princeton, Illinois: T. P. Streeter, Lessee, Republican Job Department, 1885
  PRESENTATION COPY. Rev. Stephen A. Norton from John H. Bryant, July, 1885. The author was a brother of Wm. Cullen Bryant. Not in Sturges, McKee, Harris or Maier.
  Poems on the Civil War, Lincoln, Illinois, etc.


318. BURROUGHS (REV. CHARLES). The Poetry of Religion, and Other Poems. Printed for Private Circulation. 8vo, original cloth, pp. 101.
    Boston: Ticknor, Reed, and Fields, MDCCCLI (1851)
  PRINTED FOR PRIVATE CIRCULATION. The author was an accomplished scholar and prominent in the Church and Public affairs of Portsmouth, N. H., for 45 years, being rector of St. Paul's Church in that place for the same period. Not in Sturges, McKee or Maier.


319. BUTLER (FRANCIS). First Series of Butler's Poetical Sketches . . . 12mo, original cloth, pp. [12], 1 to 107.
    Published by Francis Butler, 3 Peck Slip, New York, 1870
  Williamsburg, Long Island, Author. Contains poems: "Voyage from New York to Williamsburg;" "The Williamsburg Cars;" "The Will'sb'gh Philosopher;" etc. Not in Sturges, McKee, Harris or Maier.


320. BUTTS (ARTHUR C.). Monticello [New York]. A Picture of the Past. [In verse.] *Illustrations by W. J. Wilson.* Small 4to, cloth, pp. [5], 2 to 55.
    New York [1898]
  PRESENTATION COPY to Col. George Hart from his friend, Arthur C. Butts, October 1898. A Sullivan County, New York, Poem. Not in Sturges, McKee or Maier.

321. [CALVERT (G. H.).] Ellen: A Poem for the Times. 8vo, original cloth, pp. 48.
New York: G. W. Carleton & Co., 1867
Not in Sturges, McKee or Maier.

322. CARLETON (WILL). City Ballads. *Illustrated.* Large 8vo, original cloth, pp. 180 and 4, gilt edges.
New York: Harper & Brothers, Franklin Square, 1886
FIRST EDITION. Not in Sturges, McKee, Harris or Maier.

323. CARLETON (WILL). Farm Festivals. *Illustrated.* Large 8vo, original cloth, pp. 167 and 6, gilt edges.
New York: Harper & Brothers, Publishers [1881]
FIRST EDITION. Not in Sturges, McKee, Harris or Maier.

324. CARLETON (WILL). Rhymes of Our Planet. *Illustrations.* 8vo, original cloth, pp. VIII, one blank, [1], 2 to 195, [4 of Advertisements].
New York: Harper & Brothers, 1895
FIRST EDITION. Not in Sturges, McKee, Harris or Maier.

325. [CARLETON (WILL).] A Thanksgiving Story; embodying The Ballad of "Betsey and I Are Out" and Other Poems, by N. S. Emerson. 8vo, original cloth, pp. 200 and 4.
New York: G. W. Carleton & Co., MDCCCLXXIII [1873]
FIRST EDITION of the book that established Carleton's reputation as a poet, written under the pseudonym of N. S. Emerson. Carleton was born at Hudson, Michigan. Not in Sturges, McKee or Maier.

326. CARLETON (WILL). Young Folks' Centennial Rhymes. *Illustrated.* 8vo, original cloth, pp. 123 and 4.
New York: Harper & Brothers, Publishers, 1876
FIRST EDITION. Not in Sturges, McKee, Harris or Maier.

327. CARPENTER (WILLIAM). A Poem on the Execution of William Shaw. At Springfield, December 13th, 1770, for the Murder of Edward East in Springfield Gaol. 8vo, original boards, 6 unnumbered leaves and folding facsimiles of the original broadside poem. New York, 1916
FIRST EDITION. Not in Sturges, McKee, Harris or Maier.
Heartman Historical Series No. [21] THIRTY-ONE COPIES ONLY—published for the Original Subscribers of this series free of charge by Charles F. Heartman, 1916.
The Heartman Publications are today very scarce and in a few years very few will be obtainable, as most of them are locked up in Public institutions.

328. CARR (GEORGE P.) The Contest: A Poem. Square 16mo, original cloth, pp. 115. Chicago: P. L. Hanscom, Publisher, 1866
Poem on Abraham Lincoln and details the Battles of the Civil War in Verse. Dedicated to Maj. Gen. U. S. Volunteers, Eugene A. Carr. Not in Sturges, McKee, Harris or Maier.

## CARRIER'S ADDRESSES OF THE NEW YORK POST

329. CARRIER'S ADDRESS. To the Patrons of the New York Evening Post (as printed in the New York Herald, Jan. 4. 1803). Folio, pp. 4.
New York: [Printed & Published by Michael Burnham] 1803
Interesting political poem on Burr, Jefferson, Clinton, Livingston, also on the Western Wilds, etc. A poem of several hundred lines on the front page. Not in Sturges, McKee, Harris, Maier, New York Public Library or Wegelin.

330. CARRIER'S ADDRESS. Address of the Carrier of the New-York Evening Post to his Patrons (a poem as printed in the New York Herald, Jan. 6, 1808). Folio, pp. 4. [New-York: Printed and Published by Michael Burnham] 1808

Poem mentions Wilkinson, Judge Marshall and laws to swing Burr, trouble with England and France, Chesapeake affair, etc. Poem of over a hundred lines. Not in Sturges, McKee, Harris, Maier, New York Public Library or Wegelin.

331. CARRIER'S ADDRESS. Address of the Carrier of the New York Evening Post (a poem as printed in the New York Herald for Jan. 5, 1811). Folio, pp. 4. [New York] 1811

Poem almost entirely on Bonaparte with references to Claiborne and the conquering of Florida. Not in Sturges, McKee, Harris, Maier, New York Public Library or Wegelin.

332. [CARTER (JOHN HENTON).] Log Cabin Poems by Commodore Rollingpin. Author of "Thomas Rutherton," "Duck Creek Ballads," etc. *Portrait and illustrations.* 8vo, cloth, pp. [12], 2 to 191, [1]. St. Louis: Rollingpin Publishing Company, 1897

FIRST EDITION, see under plays for an early work by Carter ("Commodore Rollingpin"). Poems: "Back to New Orleans;" "Eugene Field," "Old Log Cabin;" "The Forty-Niner;" "Missouri Night-in-gales;" "Old Bill;" "The Mississippi;" etc. Not in Sturges, McKee or Maier.

333. [CASY (A. B.).] Florence Nightingale: or, The Angel of Charity. 8vo, original cloth, pp. 32. Brooklyn, MDCCCLVIII (1858)

Poem on the founder of the Modern Red Cross. PRIVATELY PRINTED. Not in Sturges, McKee or Harris.

334. CHARLESTON, SOUTH CAROLINA, A Satiric Poem: shewing, That Slavery still exists in a Country, which boasts, above all others of Being the Seat of Liberty. By a Westindian. 8vo, original wrappers, pp. 12 London: Published by S. Y. Collins, 1851

The author having been in Charleston about the year 1818, beheld with horror and detestation, the discipline of slavery, so gave vent to his feelings in this production. Not in Sturges, McKee, Harris, Maier, etc.

335. CHILD (Mrs. LYDIA H.). The Oasis. Edited by Mrs. Child. *Engraved portraits, views, woodcuts.* 16mo, cloth, pp. XVI and 276. Boston: Benjamin C. Bacon: 1834

Not in Sturges. SCARCE. NICE COPY. Original poem, "The Slave Ships" by Whittier; "Slave Traveler," by Miss E. H. Whittier, etc.

336. CHILDS (M. L.). Poetical Fragments by M. L. Childs. To the many Friends of My Deceased Wife who have requested copies of her Poetical Fragments, this souvenir of her is affectionately dedicated by Her Husband. 16mo, wrappers, pp. [3] and 4 to 22. [New York, 186–?]

SCARCE PRIVATELY PRINTED ITEM, lacking in Sturges, McKee, Harris, etc.

337. CHILTON (ROBERT S.). Poems. 8vo, original cloth, pp. 70. Goderich [Canada]: McGillicuddy Bros., Signal Printing House. 1885

A volume of Canadian Verse it would almost be impossible to duplicate. PRIVATELY PRINTED in a limited number for those near and dear to him. "Poem on Old Trinity Church, New York;" "Epitaph on the Tomb of [John Howard] Payne" [at Tunis]; "To James Russell Lowell," "Power's Greek Slave," "The Exile's Return," read at the Re-interment of the Remains of John Howard Payne, Author of "Home Sweet Home," at Washington, D. C., June 9th 1882; etc. Not in Sturges, Harris, McKee, Maier, etc.

338. [CLARK (W. ADOLPHUS).] Our Modern Athens; or, Who is First? A Poem by Anicetus. 8vo, cloth, pp. 70.
Boston: For Sale by Redding & Co. No 8 State Street, 1860

A poem against those miserable wretches who make money their God, whose chief pleasure in life appears to be "looking down" on their less fortunate fellow-citizens.

339. CLARKE (MARY BAYARD). Clytie and Zenobia or, The Lily and the Palm. A Poem. 8vo., original cloth, pp. 65.
New York: E. P. Dutton and Company, 1871

PRESENTATION COPY TO Mr. James E. Nash. With compliments of the Author. Dec. 15th, 1870. Not in Sturges, McKee, Harris or Maier.

### PRESENTATION COPY BY THE "MAD POET" McDONALD CLARKE

340. CLARKE (McDONALD) Death in Disguise: A Temperance Poem, From the Mss. 18mo, wrappers, pp. 36.    Boston: Published by B. B. Mussey, 1833

CHOICE COPY, with autograph inscription as follows: *W. W. Clapp From his friend the Author, Oct. 23, 1833.* Presentation copies of this author's works are rarely obtainable.

341. [CLASON (ISAAC STARR).] Don Juan. Cantos XVII-XVIII. 18mo, half old calf, marbled sides, pp. 100.
New-York: Charles Wiley, 3 Wall Street, 1825

The author, a writer of fine talent but of a dissipated life, was born in New York 1798, committed suicide in London, 1832. He appeared on the boards of the Bowery and Park Theatres, N. Y., in leading Shakespearean Parts. Don Juan was written supplementary to the poem of Lord Byron in a kindred vein, not merely of grossness but in wit. The Scandal of the author's life faithfully reflected in it added not a little to its piquancy and made a literary reputation for its author.

342. [CLASON (ISAAC STARR).] Horace in New-York. Part I (ALL PRINTED). 8vo, original wrappers, pp. 47.
New York: James M. Campbell, 87 Nassau-Street. 1826

Not in Sturges. The author satirizes or celebrates in this poem the following persons: Mad. Malabran Garcia, Doctor Mitchell, Noah, The "Mad Poet" (McDonald Clarke), "Fanny" (poem by Halleck), Emmett.

343. CLEVELAND (MRS. E. H. J.). No Sects in Heaven; and Other Poems. Square 18mo, cloth, pp. 96, gilt edges.
New York: Clark & Maynard, Publishers, 5 Barclay Street, 1869

FIRST EDITION. A famous poem, the other poems are: "The Twin Lakes in Salisbury, Connecticut;" "The Hidden Path, or The Atlantic Cable;" and others of Connecticut interest, etc. Not in Sturges, McKee or Maier.

344. [CLIFFTON (WILLIAM).] The Baviad and Maeviad. By William Gifford, Esquire [5 lines latin verse] To which is prefixed, A Poetical Epistle to the Author by An American Gentleman [i. e.] William Cliffton. A New Edition Revised. 12mo. boards, red roan back, pp. XX, [3], 2 to 145.
London, Printed, Philadelphia: Re-printed for William Cobbett.
MDCCXCIX (1799)

RARE VOLUME, lacking in the Sturges, McKee, Harris and Maier collections.

345. CLIFFTON (WILLIAM). Poems, Chiefly Occasional, by the late Mr. Cliffton. To which are prefixed, introductory notices of the Life, Character and
[Continued

Writings of the Author, and *An Engraved Likeness*. (*Field Pinxt. D. Edwin, Sc.*) 18mo, old tree calf, pp. XVIII, 119 and [1].

New-York: Printed for J. W. Fenno, by G. & R. Waite. 1800

Cliffton, a Quaker, was born in Philadelphia, in 1772, and died in 1799, from consumption, at the age of 27 years. The major portion of his works are of a satirical nature. The volume contains his poems: "The Group," "Song [sung in Philadelphia] on Lord Nelson's Victory;" Song, "Soul of Columbia;" "Address of the Devil to the United Irish Men;" "Answer of the United Irishmen to an Address from the Devil;" "Descent of Talleyrand into Hell;" etc. Not in Sturges. An interesting volume of verse.

346. COLE ("THE MAD-HOUSE LYRIST"). Mad-House Lyrics. A Selection of Poems from the Diary of Cole: Ex-King of the Larder, now Mad-House Lyrist. 32mo, original printed wrappers, pp. 48.

Published by the Author, Concord: New Hampshire Steam Printing Works.

1852

Another poet who lost his mind. On page 14 the poet versifies his trouble, as follows:

> "My mind is discomposed I cannot write
> Upon any subject either new or trite,
> But still to shew the passionate desire,
> I have for strumming on Parnassus' lyre,
> A War I'll wage against that vexation,
> Which hugs me heavier than hell's damnation,
> And scribble out a verse, one two or three
> To keep alive my singularity," etc.

Extremely scarce, not in Sturges, McKee, etc.

### SCARCE REPRINT OF AN EXCESSIVELY RARE COLONIAL POEM

347. COLLECTION (A) of Elegiac Poems: devoted to the memory of the late virtuous and excellent Matron and worthy Elder in the Church of Christ [of the Society of Friends] Martha Thomas. Late wife of Rees Thomas of Merion, in the County of Philadelphia, in the Province of Pennsylvania: and daughter of William Aubrey, of Llan Elew, in the County of Brecknock, in Great Britain, who departed this life, on the 7th. of the Twelfth Month, 1726–27 . . . 16mo, original cloth, pp. 16.

Philadelphia: Printed by Samuel Keimer, in Second Street. MDCCXXVII.

Reprinted by Lydia R. Bailey, 1837

PRESENTATION COPY from Mary Jones the editoress of this second edition. Evans gives title but no collation which indicates he has never seen a copy of the original edition, which leaves the above reprint (which is also rare) as the only form of this poem obtainable for collectors of American Verse.

Not in Sturges, Harris, McKee, Maier or New York Public Library List.

348. COLMAN (JAMES F.). The Island Bride, and Other Poems. 12mo, original boards, pp. 164.　　　　　　Boston: William D. Ticknor & Co. [1846]

Not in Sturges, McKee or Maier.

349. [CONNER (JAMES).] The Garland; for 1831, designed as a Christmas and New Year's Present. *Engraved plates*. 12mo, calf, pp. 324.

New York: C. H. Peabody. 1831

This volume contains the choicest pieces which have appeared in the *Token* and *Legendary* with the author's names attached. Fiction and Verse on Col. Boone, Catskill Mountains, Indians, Saratoga Battlefield, Legend of the Notch (N. H.), etc. Not in Sturges, McKee, Harris or Maier.

350. COLMAN (BENJAMIN) A Poem on Elijah's Translation, Occasioned by the Death of the Reverend and Learned Mr. Samuel Willard, Late Pastor to a Church of Christ in Boston, and Vice-President of Harvard College in Cambridge. By Mr. Colman, V. D. M. . . . . 18mo, pp. [2] and 14.

Boston: Printed for Benjamin Eliot, 1707

A POEM
ON
ELIJAHS Tranflation,
Occasion'd by the DEATH of the
Reverend and Learned
Mr. SAMUEL WILLARD,

Late *Paftor* to a Church of CHRIST
in *Bofton*, and *Vice-Prefident* of
*Harvard Colledge* in *Cambridge*.

By Mr. COLMAN, *V. D. M.*

*Cœlo Mufa beat.* Hor.Carm.Lib.4.Od.8.
----*Nec meus audet*
*Rem tentare pudor, quam Vires ferre re-*
[ *cufent.*
Hor. Ep. 1. Lib. 2.

*BOSTON*:
Printed for *Benjamin Eliot*, 1707.

[No. 350]

VERY RARE. Not in Sturges or New York Public Library catalogues. Dr. Colman the author, Pastor of the Brattle Street Church, Boston, attained some recognition as a poet with his very creditable poem on Willard—a poem in which Willard's life is likened to that of Elijah. The versification is smooth, and the description of the heavenly ascension is unusually good. The above poem is the only separately printed volume of verse by Colman—he wrote a few minor poems which were printed in his Life by Turrell in 1749.

[See facsimile]

351. [CONRAD (R.).] Poems: By a Friend. 8vo, cloth, pp. 129.

West Chester, Pa.: F. S. Hickman, Printer and Publisher, 1875

QUAKER VERSE. Not in Sturges, McKee, Harris or Maier.

## AMERICA'S QUEEREST POET, PRINTER AND ARTIST: THE REV. WM. COOK OF SALEM, MASS.

The most curious books in this collection are the following 23 items by the Rev. William Cook, printed at Salem, written in a most villainous verse, printed on different sorts of paper, with the poorest of type, and illustrated with barbarous woodcuts, done by the Author, who was his own printer, illustrator and in some cases a hand-color artist of the crudest type. Cook certainly is the most amusing of American Poets. The famous Sturges Collection of American Verse lately sold contained but one title by this author—McKee had none—the Harris Collection Catalogue lists three,—in fact it seems as if no really large collection of Cook's writings exists —altho he must have written and issued at least fifty titles—therefore it behooves the wise collector to make good use of this rare opportunity to secure some of this author's works.

352. COOK (WILLIAM). The Bank. By Rev. William Cook, A.B. Author of the Fragments, The Neriah, and the Eucleia. *2 plates.* 12mo, yellow illustrated wrappers, pp. 22. Salem, November, 1862

> Poem in 8 scenes with choruses. The Fifth scene reads in part:
>
> > "O'er California-rock-rents,
> > To make miners gain,
> > On roll the waves down rush the torrents
> > Whence we Bank-Stock obtain,"
> > etc., etc., etc.
>
> Not in Sturges.

353. COOK (WILLIAM). College, Fourth Part of the Cor. Felix—Ten Parts, by Rev. William Cook, A.B. Author of The Eucleia—Ten Parts—The Neriah —Four Parts—The Guides—Ten Parts. *Woodcut view on title and 3 plates.* 12mo, brown wrappers, pp. [1], 84 to 92. Poem on inside of both wrappers. Salem, August, 1871

> The views are of Phillips Academy, Andover, Mass., Yale College, and Trinity College, Hartford, Conn. Not in Sturges, etc.

354. COOK (WILLIAM). The Columbia An Address [in Verse] by Rev. William Cook, A. B. before the Columbian Association delivered Salem, August 22, 1863. Ex glande quercus, ex virtute vis est. Translation, From acorn to oak, from virtue is the force. *2 plates and woodcut on title.* 12mo, brown wrappers, pp. 8. Salem, 1863 & 4

> One plate is a view of Liberty Street, Salem, Mass. Poem, "The Yankee Troops' Paean," and "Columbia." Not in Sturges.

355. COOK (WILLIAM). The Correspondent, Third Part of the Cor Felix.—Ten Parts. By Rev. William Cook, A. B. Author of the Eucleia—Ten Parts—The Neriah—Four Parts—The Guides—Ten Parts. *Woodcut on front wrapper and 3 plates.* 12mo, green wrappers. Salem, April, 1870

> Each plate is entitled "A View from Castle Hill," but taken from 3 different points. One poem included in above was written by Cook as early as 1834. Not in Sturges.

356. COOK (WILLIAM). Dona Bona. First Division of First Part of the Cor Felix—Ten Parts by Rev. William Cook, A.B. Author of the Eucleia—Ten Parts—The Neriah—Four Parts—The Guides—Ten Parts. *3 plates, woodcut on front wrapper.* 12mo, green wrappers, pp. 20 including wrappers and plates. Several poems on inside of wrappers. Salem, June, 1869

> Plates are entitled: "While the Canoe was pushed from Shore Harbor Fire;" "State Normal School, Salem. Poem on Lake Chochorna" [Indian Poem]; Poem, "Harbour Fire, burning of a Salem Packet Ship," etc. Not in Sturges.

357. COOK (WILLIAM). The Eudromia. By Rev. William Cook, A. B. Author of the Liturgy, Potsandove, The Result, The Bank, The Fragments, The Neriah, and the Eucleia. *Frontispiece plate and ornamental title cut on front wrapper.* 12mo, gray wrappers, pp. 6. Salem, March, 1866

> Eudromia means Good Running. The Angel in the illustration presents to Eudromia or Good Runner the meros or life potion. Not in Sturges.

358. COOK (WILLIAM). The Firemen's Liturgy, By Rev. William Cook A. B. Author of Potsandove, The Result, The Bank, The Fragments, The Neriah, and the Eucleia. *3 fine street views in Salem.* 12mo, dark pink wrappers, pp. 10. Salem, August, 1865

> Not in Sturges.

359. COOK (WILLIAM). The Fragments. By Rev. William Cook, A. B. Author of The Eucleia and The Neriah. *3 illustrations counting wrapper.* 12mo, brown wrappers, pp. [2], 16 to 17, [1], 4 to 14, 11 to 20.

Salem, March, 186[2]

> PERFECT COPY. Cook's pamphlets are always oddly numbered. The first poem is entitled, "Fremont," and reads (part of first stanza):
>
> "Lo, yonder through the distant groves
> Th' raging buffaloes came—
> Rolling dust and bellowing sound
> Told that they were not fondly tame
> That they were not gentle as doves,
> As dashed the hunters through the groves," etc.
>
> Second Stanza in part:
> "On, on to the Forks of the Platte . . .,
> Midst joys or, through sufferings great . . .,
> On, on to Oregon's Great Gate . . ." etc.
> Not in Sturges.

360. COOK (WILLIAM). The Hearttrier. By Rev. William Cook, A. B. Author of the Motiveboat, Lillygrow, The Eudromia, The Firemen's Liturgy, Potsandove, The Result, The Columbia, The Bank, The Fragments, The Neriah, and the Eucleia. *2 plates and cut on front wrapper.* 12mo, wrappers, pp. 18. Salem, May, 1867

> One plate is a view of "Winter's Island." Poem on the Irish emigrants that were landed on "Winter's Island" from the Salem Packet Ships. Not in Sturges.

361. COOK (WILLIAM). Hope. By Rev. William Cook, 1852–1859. Latin. In Christo spes est opulentis. The Translation, Faith in Christ is opulence. 16mo, wrappers, pp. 18. [Salem] 1859

Not illustrated as usual. Judging from the Latin quotation on title our poet friend Cook was quite a scholar as well as a poet prodigy. Not in Sturges, etc.

362. COOK (WILLIAM). Lillygrow. By Rev. William Cook, A. B. Author of the Hearttrier, The Motiveboat, The Eudromia, The Firemen's Liturgy, Potsandove, The Result, The Columbia, The Bank, The Fragments, The Neriah, and the Eucleia. *Plate and cut on front wrapper.* 12mo, wrappers, pp. 8. Salem, May, 1867

Not in Sturges.

363. COOK (WILLIAM). Martyn. Sixth Part of The Cor Felix—Ten Parts, By Rev. William Cook, A. B. Author of The Eucleia,—Ten Parts,—The Neriah,—Four Parts,—The Guides,—Ten Parts. *3 illustrations and cut on title.* 12mo, original wrappers, pp. [1], 126 to 136. Salem, June, 1873

Not in Sturges, Harris, McKee or Maier.

364. COOK (WILLIAM). The Motiveboat. By Rev. William Cook, A. B. Author of The Hearttrier, Lillygrow, The Eudromia, The Firemen's Liturgy, Pots-andove, The Result, The Columbia, The Bank, The Fragments, The Neriah and the Eucleia. *Plate, "So the Post Boy Tempting the Shannon," and woodcut on front wrapper.* 12mo, wrappers, pp. 8. Salem, May, 1867

Poem gives an account of the *Post Boy* tempting the British War Ship *Shannon* to give chase and fire her cannons, leaving the way clear for the *Constitution* to conquer the *Guerrière.* The *Post Boy* was commanded by the author's father. Not in Sturges.

365. COOK (WILLIAM). The Neriah, Part First for The Metrical Apocalypse, from the Greek Prose-Text, Composed, Illustrated & Published solely by Rev. William Cook, A. B. Author of Chestnut Street, Fremont, The Telegraph, or Star-Banner Song, The Ploughboy, Olive Grove, Etc. *Four plates, cut on wrapper title and facsimile of a Greek Logos.* 12mo, original wrappers, pp. 39. Salem, February, 1858

The author has copyrighted in Massachusetts the four parts of the Neriah. The only publication by Cook with a copyright notice. The title means the "Lamp of the Lord." Not in Sturges, McKee, Harris or Maier.
The author finished and printed one part each for four years, 1858 to 1861.

366. COOK (WILLIAM). The Neriah, Part Second [balance of title same as first part]. *Five plates and cut on front wrapper title.* 12mo, original wrappers, pp. [3], notice slip by author, 44 to 82. Salem, March, 1859

Not in Sturges, Harris, McKee or Maier.

367. COOK (WILLIAM). The Neriah, Part Third [balance of title same as first part]. *Five plates and cut on wrapper title.* 12mo, original wrappers, pp. [2], 85 to 120. Salem, May, 1860

Some of the plates depict the Fall of Babylon and the Wreck of its Commerce. Not in Sturges, McKee, Harris or Maier.

368. COOK (WILLIAM). The Neriah, Part Fourth [balance of title same as first part]. *Five plates and cut on title.* 12mo, original wrappers, pp. [2], 123 to 160. Salem, March, 1861

A few of the plates in this number would give some people the horrors. Not in Sturges, McKee, Harris or Maier.

369. COOK (WILLIAM). The Ploughboy. A Poem, Part First. By Rev. William Cook. Author of Olive Grove, Etc. *Illustrated.* 16mo, sewed, pp. 32.

Salem, 1854

Illustrations are Cottage by the Moor, The Ploughboy, Grandam Knitting Socks, Then drove she from the Mill, The Children found him tame (the freak horse), The Ploughboy charmed his maid (by playing the flute), and Ellen (evidently the Ploughboy's maid). Not in Sturges, etc.

370. COOK (WILLIAM). The Ploughboy. A Poem, Part Third, composed, illustrated & published solely by Rev. William Cook. Author of Olive Grove, etc. *8 illustrations.* 16mo, sewed, pp. [8] and 45 to 62 and [2].

Salem, 1855

PLAIN BLACK, SMALL ISSUE. Not in Sturges, etc.

371. COOK (WILLIAM). The Ploughboy. A Poem. Part Third, composed, illustrated & published solely by Rev. William Cook. Author of Olive Grove, etc. *With 11 illustrations, including wrapper.* 12mo, colored illustrated wrappers, pp. [1]–70 to 107.

Salem, 1855

THE RARE COLORED ISSUE, LARGER IN SIZE, with different pagination, and an additional poem. Not in Sturges, etc.

372. COOK (WILLIAM). Potsandove. By Rev. William Cook, A. B. Author of The Result, The Bank, The Fragments, The Neriah, and the Eucleia. *2 illustrations including wrapper cut.* 12mo, light yellow wrappers, pp. 15.

Salem, July, 1864

"Among the Pots" is the title of the quaint cut of a New England kitchen. Not in Sturges.

373. COOK (WILLIAM). The Result. By Rev. William Cook, A. B. Author of The Bank, The Fragments, The Neriah, and the Eucleia. *2 illustrations including wrapper cut.* 12mo, brown wrappers, pp. 12.     Salem, May, 1863

Washington's Birthday Sermon, with poem on last page. Not in Sturges.

374. COOK (WILLIAM). Woman, Second Part. Ninth Part of the Cor Felix—Ten Parts, By Rev. William Cook, A. B. Author of the Eucleia—Ten Parts, The Neriah—Four Parts—The Guides—Ten Parts. *With 4 illustrations including wrapper.* 12mo, colored illustrated wrappers, pp. [1], 192 to 206.     Salem, February, 1876

Not in Sturges, etc.

375. COOKE (HELEN M.—"Lottie Linwood"). Gold-Thread and Other Poems. 16mo, original cloth, pp. 195.

New-York: E. B. Treat, 805 Broadway, 1874

Contains, ORIGINAL PHOTOGRAPH of authoress, autographed. Dedicated to Chancellor O. S. Halstead of New Jersey. Not in Sturges, McKee, Harris or Maier.

376. COOKE (ROSE TERRY). Smith College Commencement, 1881. June 22. The Spiritual Element in Study: An Oration by Alexander McKenzie. POEM by Rose Terry Cooke. 8vo, printed wrappers, pp. 24.

Northampton, Mass., 1881

Mrs. Cooke's poem is entitled, "The Flower Sower." Not in Sturges, Harris, McKee, Maier, etc.

58

377. [COXE (A. C.).] Halloween, A Romaunt with Lays, Meditative and Devotional. By the author of "Christian Ballads." *Engraved frontispiece by Gimbrede.* 32mo, original cloth, gilt edges, pp. 189, [1].
Hartford: H. S. Parsons, 1845
A very scarce little volume by Bishop Coxe. Not in Sturges, Harris, McKee or Maier.

378. CRANCH (CHRISTOPHER P.). Poems. 8vo, original boards, pp. 116.
Philadelphia: Carey and Hart, 1844
FIRST EDITION, PRESENTATION COPY. Not in Sturges collection.

379. CURREY (AUGUSTUS). The Sower. A Poem. *Illustrated.* 4to, cloth, 15 leaves.
Detroit, Michigan [1884]
PRESENTATION COPY. To Mr. and Mrs. Geo. Clark, with the best wishes of Mr. and Mrs. Augustus Curry. Detroit, April 15, 1891. Portrait of author and part of a broadside poem pasted in. Not in Sturges, McKee, Harris or Maier.

380. CUTTER (BLOODGOOD H.). The Long Island Farmer's Poems. Lines written on the "Quaker City" Excursion to Palestine, and Other Poems. *Portrait.* 8vo, cloth, pp. 499, [3 of contents].
New York: N. Tibbals & Sons. 124 Nassau Street. (Published for the Author.) [1886]
The author was Mark Twain's "Larriat" in "Innocents Abroad." These are his collected poems (500 pages) to 1886. SCARCE. Not in Sturges, Harris or Maier.

381. CUTTER (G. W.). Buena Vista: and Other Poems. *Fine mezzotint portrait by E. C. Hawkins.* 12mo, cloth, pp. 168. Top margins water-stained.
Cincinnati: Morgan & Overend, Printers, 1848
ISSUED BY SUBSCRIPTION—SCARCE, not in Sturges. Covington, Ky., author. Poems on Henry Clay, Death of Osceola, Grande Prairie, Land of the West, Mexican War, etc.

382. DANA (JOSEPH). A New American Selection of Lessons in Reading and Speaking. Consisting of Sacred Moral and Historical extracts; Humorous, Entertaining, and Descriptive Pieces; Select sentences, and Maxims; Poetry, Dialogues, &c. To which are added, Elements of Gesture. *Illustrated with Four Copperplate Engravings.* Published according to Act of Congress. Third Edition, Corrected and Improved. 12mo, old calf, pp. 30.
Printed at Exeter, by H. Ranlet, For Thomas and Andrews . . . Jan., 1799
American poems: "Hymn to the Deity" (by Gov. Livingston of N. J.); "Creation" (by Dwight); "Address to the Sun;" "Address to the Moon" (by Sewall); "Description of the First American Congress" (verse by Barlow); "Columbia," (by Dwight). A rare American Reader. Not in Sturges, McKee, Harris or Maier.

383. DANA (MARY S. B.). The Parted Family, and Other Poems. 8vo, cloth, pp. 312.
New York: Dayton & Saxton, 1842
By the author of "The Southern Harp." Not in Sturges, McKee, Harris or Maier

384. DAYTON (LAURA C. S.). Deth. 18mo, original cloth, pp. 16.
New York: Brentano's Literary Emporium, 39 Union Square, 1878
A sad love story in Verse of Farmer Fielding's daughter, the time about ten years after the Revolutionary War. Not in Sturges, McKee, Harris or Maier.

385. DENISON (CHARLES W.). The American Village; and Other Poems. *Engraved frontispiece.* 18mo, original cloth, pp. 143.

Boston: Henry Skinner & Co., 1845

FIRST EDITION. Not in Sturges, McKee or Maier.

386. DENKSPRUCHE für Schulkinder gesammelt. [By "Eine deutschen Frau," Cincinnati, 1873.] 16mo, original cloth, pp. 79.

Cincinnati: Im Verlag von A. E. Wilde [1873]

VERY SCARCE. German American Poems. Contains 50-stanza poem by the authoress, who calls herself "Eine Deutschen Frau." Not in Sturges, McKee, Harris or Maier.

387. DENSLOW (VAN BUREN). Manhatta; A Legend of the Hudson. 18mo, original cloth, pp. [5] and 4 to 132.

New York: H. Dayton, 79 John Street, 1856

A poem on the Hudson River Indians. Not in Sturges, Harris, McKee or Maier.

388. DENTON (WILLIAM). Poems for Reformers; Second edition. 12mo, original cloth, pp. 118.

Printed for the Author, at the "Vanguard" Office, 109 Lake Street, Cleveland, O., 1859

A rare volume of very unusual verse. PRESENTATION COPY. Not in Sturges, McKee or Maier.

389. DIADEM (THE), for MDCCCXLVI. A Present for All Seasons. *With ten engravings, after pictures by Inman, Leutze, etc., and engraved half-title.* Large 4to, original cloth, pp. 96.          Philadelphia: Carey & Hart, 1846

Outside of its poetical interest, this volume contains 10 portraits and figures, the finest examples of Sartain's artistic mezzotint plates, one being a portrait of Carey, the publisher, who died before this work was finished. It contains 3 poems by Emerson. RARE, not in Sturges, McKee, Harris or Maier.

390. DIX (JOHN E.). Pastime Sketches. Small 4to, original cloth, pp. 35.

Newark, N. J.: Edwin A. Dix, Printer, No. 444 High Street, 1877

Poems: "Niagara;" "The Recluse of Niagara;" "On the Beach at Long Branch;" "Vision of Niagara;" etc. The verses are all on Niagara, or Long Branch, New Jersey. Not in Sturges, McKee, Harris or Maier.

391. DIX (WILLIAM GILES). The Deck of the Crescent City. A Poem. Part First [ALL PRINTED]. 12mo, original printed wrappers. pp. 46.

Boston and Cambridge: James Munroe and Company, 1852

Poem on Texas and Mexico with mention of Longfellow, Harvard College, Franklin, etc. Not in Sturges, McKee or Maier.

392. DONALDSON (SAMUEL J., JR.). Lyrics and Other Poems. 8vo, original cloth, pp. 208.          Philadelphia: Lindsay & Blakiston, 1860

"Poem on Fanny Kemble;" "Hymn to the Catholic Church;" "Sonnet to Fanny Kemble;" "Dialogue between the Poet and his Lyre;" etc. Not in Sturges, McKee or Maier. PRESENTATION COPY TO *Mr. George S. McKay from his friend Saml. J. Donaldson, Jr.*

393. DONNELLY (ELEANOR C.). The Children of the Golden Sheaf, and other Poems. Small 4to, original cloth, pp. [4], 3 to 64. (One page spotted.)

[Philadelphia, 1884]

PRESENTATION COPY. PRIVATELY PRINTED. *Miss Tillie May Forney with the affectionate regards of the Authoress. Philadelphia, Aug. 14, 84.* Not in Sturges, McKee, Harris or Maier.

394. DONNELLY (ELEANOR C.). Out of Sweet Solitude. 8vo, original cloth, pp. 105. Philadelphia: J. B. Lippincott & Co., 1873

> Minnesota and Pennsylvania Catholic Poet. Contains a special section, "Poems of the Civil War." Not in Sturges, McKee, Harris or Maier.

395. DUGANNE (A. J. H.). Injuresoul; A Satire for Science. 8vo, original cloth, pp. 214. New-York: American Book-Print Company, 1884

> Anti-Robert G. Ingersoll and Tom Paine item by a Catholic poet. Not in Sturges, McKee, Harris or Maier.

396. DUTCHER (J. W.). Narrative of the Mysterious Can, illustrative of the Washington Reform, to which is appended the Temperance Platform. 18mo, boards, pp. [3], 4 to 104.
[Amenia, N. Y.] Printed at the Amenia Times Office, 1854

> A VERY SCARCE DUTCHESS COUNTY TEMPERANCE POEM.

397. [DWIGHT (TIMOTHY).] A Select Collection of Poems, and other Elegant Poetical Extracts, on subjects Micellaneous, Moral, and Religious, by the most celebrated authors from Pope, Goldsmith, Blair, [7 others], Dwight, &c. 12mo, original boards, uncut edges, pp. 298 and [2 of contents].
Boston: Printed for Joseph Bumstead, 1807

> Dwight is the only American named on title-page, his well known poem "Columbia" being included. Among the other American verse is included "Yankee Doodle or a Journey to Camp;" "Lines on the Religious Attention in Vermont;" "The Deserted House" by an American; "Description of Charlestown;" "The Charleston, South-Carolina Ladies met by an inebriated Son of Neptune;" "To the Rev. Dr. Watts," by Byles; "On Washington's Address on the Resignation of his Office;" etc., etc. Not in Sturges, McKee, Harris, Maier or New York Public Library.

398. [EASTMAN (MARY H.).] Jenny Wade of Gettysburg. 8vo, original cloth, pp. 33. Philadelphia: J. B. Lippincott & Co., 1864

> PRESENTATION COPY from the Authoress to her Son. Jenny Wade was baking bread for the Soldiers at the Battle of Gettysburg when a bullet pierced her heart. She was situated between the Rebel and Union Lines and had been ordered away by the Rebels but she refused to go for patriotic reasons. Not in Sturges, McKee, Harris or Maier.

399. ECHOES of Nature. 8vo, original white boards, and title-label, pp. 140.
Philadelphia: E. C. & J. Biddle, 1845

> Poems: "Niagara;" "Laura Bridgman;" "The Barefoot Boy;" "The White Mountains;" etc. Not in Sturges, McKee or Maier.

400. EDDY (MARY BAKER). Christ and Christmas, A Poem by Reverend Mary Baker G. Eddy, Author of "Science and Health with Key to the Scriptures," and Other Works. Third edition revised. *Illustrated.* Oblong 8vo, pp. [55].
Pleasant View, Concord, New Hampshire, 1897

> The illustrations (in a black and white lithograph) by Mrs. Eddy and J. F. Gilman are Christian Science propaganda of her volume "Science and Health." Edward N. Pearson, was the Printer. Without a doubt PRIVATELY PRINTED AND RARE. Not in Sturges, McKee or Maier.

401. [ELLENWOOD (HENRY S.).] Granny Jackson's Lullaby to Little Martin . . . A New Song for the Political Nursery. By Peter Pindar, Jr. 8vo, sewed, pp. [1], 33 to 38.
United States Telegraph Extra. Washington, September 17, 1832

> A SCARCE POLITICAL POEM on Jackson and Van Buren. Not in Sturges, Harris, McKee, Maier, etc.

## THE RAREST VOLUME OF OHIO AND VERMONT VERSE

Including also Sketches, written on the spot, of the then Ohio Settlements of Marietta, Cincinnati, Greenville,—on the country between Forts Washington and Hamilton, and on the country between Forts Hamilton and Greenville, *and still further including:*—A First hand narrative of the author's Adventures in the Indian Campaign, on the Western Frontier, under General Wayne until the Treaty of Peace with the Indians.

402. ELLIOT (JAMES). The Poetical and Miscellaneous Works of James Elliot, Citizen of Guilford, Vermont, and late A Noncommissioned Officer in the Legion of the United States. In Four Books. [12 line verse from Pope.] 12mo. old sheep, pp. 271 and 5-page "List of Subscribers" and Errata. Greenfield, Massachusetts, Printed by Thomas Dickman, for the Author. M,DCC,XCVIII (1798)

T H E

POETICAL AND MISCELLANEOUS

# W O R K S

O F

# *JAMES ELLIOT,*

CITIZEN OF GUILFORD, VERMONT,

AND LATE

A NONCOMMISSIONED OFFICER IN THE

LEGION OF THE UNITED STATES.

IN FOUR BOOKS.

Nor Fame I flight, nor feather favours call,
She comes unlook'd for, if she comes at all
But, if the purchase cost so dear a price,
As foothing folly, or exalting vice;
And, if the Muse must flatter lawless fway,
And follow still where fortune leads the way;
Or, if no basis bear my rising name,
But the fall'n ruins of another's fame;—
Then teach me, Heav'n, to scorn the guilty bays,
Drive from my breast that wretched lust of praise.
Unblemish'd let me live, or die unknown:
O GRANT ME HONEST FAME, OR GRANT ME
NONE!

POPE.

GREENFIELD, MASSACHUSETTS.
PRINTED BY THOMAS DICKMAN,
FOR THE AUTHOR.

M,DCC,XCVIII.

[No. 402]

ONLY 300 COPIES WERE PRINTED BY SUBSCRIPTION. This volume is so rare that Gilman, in his Vermont Bibliography states he has taken the title from Sabin. Not in McKee, Sturges, Harris, Maier, New York Public Library, etc.

Some of the historical poems are: "Lines on the Adoption of the Federal Constitution by Vermont;" "Progress of Freedom: Or, A View of the Heroes and Martyrs of Liberty: An Ode;" "Elegy, Commemorative of the expedition of Brigadier General Harmar into the Indian country Northwest of the Ohio in the autumn of 1790; and the defeat of a detachment from his Army, commanded by Major Wyllys of the 1st U. S. Regiment;" written at Fort Washington, on the Ohio—Feb. 2, 1795; "Elegy,

[*Continued*

[ No. 402.   ELLIOT (JAMES)—*Continued* ]

descriptive of the defeat of the American Army, under General St. Clair, by the Indians, on the 4th of November, 1791," written near the fatal spot; "Lines, Commemorative of the victory obtained by General Wayne and his gallant army, over the whole hostile force of the united Indian nations, northwest of the Ohio, near the British Fort Miami, on the 20th of August, 1794—and the consequent treaty of peace—in the following year," written at Greenville, Head Quarters of the Legion of the United States, etc., etc.

[See facsimile]

403.   EMMONS (WILLIAM). An Oration and [National] Poem delivered July 4, 1826, being the Fiftieth Anniversary of American Independence. Second Edition. 8vo, sewed, pp. 16.                    Boston: Published by the Author, 1826

PRIVATELY PRINTED. Not in Sturges, Harris, McKee or Maier. Fine copy, altho a portion of Oration leaf is gone. A poem celebrating the American Revolution and the War of 1812.

404.   EMMONS (WILLIAM). An Oration [in Prose and Verse] pronounced at the Washington Garden, By William Emmons, Born, Feb. 27, 1792. Native Citizen of the City of Boston. July 4, 1829. 8vo, original wrappers, pp. 16.
                    Boston: Published for the Author July 10, 1829

The outside of wrappers are entirely written on in the handwriting of the author being a PRESENTATION INSCRIPTION to the author's friend J. E. Glover. PRIVATELY PRINTED and VERY RARE, no copy located in Sturges and other collections.

405.   EVEREST (C. W.). The Primrose: A Gift of Friendship. Edited by Rev. C. W. Everest [4 lines verse]. *Lithographic Farming Scene frontispiece.* 32mo, original cloth, pp. 128.                    Hartford: Henry S. Parsons, 1848

FIRST EDITION. A scarce volume by the author of "Poets of Connecticut." Not in Sturges, Harris, McKee or Maier.

406.   EVERYTHING SERENE [A conversation (in verse) between Two Citizens About Public Affairs]. New York, July, 1871. 8vo. original wrappers, pp. 28.
                    [New York, 1871]

Dedicated to the Railroad Kings. On the rotten politics, Railroad Monopoly (Cooke's Northern Pacific R. R.), etc. Ends with the following lines:

"But in the gentle language of John Hay,
They'll wrestle their hash in hell some quiet day."

VERY SCARCE. No copy located in Sturges, McKee, Harris, Maier, etc.

407.   FAIR CIRCASSIAN, A Poem; imitated from The Songs of Solomon. If a Man would give all the substance of his house for Love it would utterly be contemned. Sol. Songs, c.vii:v.7. 16mo, unbound, pp. [2] and 32.
                    New-York: Printed for the Amateurs of the Fine Arts.   1795

AN EXTREMELY RARE POEM, lacking in the Sturges and other American collections of verse. Otis in his *History of American Verse 1625–1807* does not mention this item, although he made a special effort to locate new titles not in Wegelin.

408.   FAIRFIELD (SUMNER LINCOLN). The Last Night of Pompeii; A Poem: and Lays and Legends. 8vo, original boards, pp. 309
                    New York.  Printed by Elliott and Palmer, 20 William-Street.
                    MDCCCXXXII (1832)

Other poems included are: "Urn Burial;" "Sachem's Chant (on the Mochican-hittuck, *i. e.* the Hudson River);" and "Walter Colebrooke, A Tale" (in prose of New England). Not in Sturges collection.

409.   FAWCETT (EDGAR). Fantasy and Passion. 12mo. cloth, pp. XI, [4], 4to to 191.
                    Boston. Roberts Brothers.  1878

FIRST EDITION. Not in Sturges or McKee.

410. FENNO (MISS J.—of Boston). Original Compositions in Prose and Verse, on Subjects Moral and Religious. 18mo, old calf, pp. 116.

Wrentham (Mass.), Printed by Nathaniel Heaton, Jun. 1803

Preface dated 1791. The authoress' poem "On the President of the United States" (Great Washington); "On the death of Rev. Thomas Gair, Pastor Second Baptist Church, Boston;" etc. Not in Sturges, McKee, Maier, nor does the New York Public Library catalogue list this edition.

411. FERRIS (MRS. MORRIS PATTERSON). A Legend of New Year Eve. A. D. MDCCCXCVI. Oblong 18mo, 8 leaves. [New York, 1896]

PRIVATELY PRINTED POEM on early Dutch Life in New York. Dedicated to the Colonial Dames of New York. Not in Sturges, McKee or Maier.

412. [FESSENDEN (THOMAS G.).] Terrible Tractoration, and Other Poems. By Christopher Caustic, M. D. Fellow of the Royal College of Physicians Aberdeen, and Honorary Member of no less than Nineteen very learned Societies, Fourth American Edition. To which is prefixed Caustic's Wooden Book-sellers and Miseries of Authorship. 16mo, boards, pp. xi.

Boston: Samuel Colman, 1837

Written for the last edition of Tractoration, but omitted with the hope that reformation might supersede the necessity of castigation. A VERY SCARCE ELEVEN-PAGE TRACT IN VERSE. The RAREST OF THE FESSENDEN SERIES. Not in Sturges, Harris, McKee or Maier.

413. FEW (A) FAMILIAR GLANCES at Matters And Things in General and some in Particular, respectfully inscribed, with the Compliments of the Season to the Patrons of the Salem Register, by the Carriers thereof. January 1, 1858. 8vo, sewed, pp. 8. Salem [1857]

Treats of events of the year in Massachussetts, the United States and elsewhere, a few lines quoted here and there may interest the reader, viz.:

"The Red horse Kansas showing all his bones
Pummeled by demagogues with clubs and stones."
* * *
Hark! Like a Clarion, echoing thro' the West,
The Mormon Rooster crows from out his nest."
* * *
"Westward the course of Empire takes its way,
Swift as a hen-thief in a 2 hoss shay."

And other events of the year treated in similar verse. Not in Sturges, McKee, Harris or Maier.

414. [FIELD (JOSEPH M.).] La Déesse, an Elssler-atic Romance. By the Author of "Straws". 8vo, original cloth, pp. 44.

New York: Carvill & Co. 108 Broadway. 1841

Poem on the noted German Dancer who was the rage in New York at that period. A Satire in verse against Fanny and her lovers. Not in Sturges, Harris, McKee or Maier.

415. FIELD (MAUNSELL B.). Occasional Verses. . . 4to, wrappers, pp. 17.

[New York, 1863?]

VERY SCARCE, PRIVATELY PRINTED in facsimile of author's manuscript. Not in Sturges, McKee, Harris or Maier collections.

416. FLAGG (ISAAC). Pedantic Versicles. 12mo, original cloth, pp. [7], 6 to 92, gilt edges. Boston: Ginn, Heath & Co., 1883

FIRST EDITION, not in Sturges, McKee, Harris or Maier.

417. FLAGG (WILSON). The Tailor's Shop: or Crowns of Thorns and Coats of Thistles, designed to Tickle Some and Nettle Others; intended chiefly for Politicians, inscribed to those whom they may fit. 16mo, original printed wrappers, pp. 58.                    Boston: Hotchkiss & Company, 1844
By the "Essex County Thoreau."

418. FLEET (SAMUEL). The Long-Island Journal of Philosophy and Cabinet of Variety, conducted by Samuel Fleet. Assisted by a number of literary gentlemen. For December . . . 1825. Vol. I. Number 8. 8vo, original printed wrappers, pp. [1] and 338 to 384, uncut edges.
Huntington (L. I.), Printed by Hiram Hershell [1825]
View of Huntington Academy across back wrapper. AN EXCEEDINGLY RARE LONG ISLAND IMPRINT AND PERIODICAL. Contains: Pinckney's poem, "Italy," page 380–81. Choice copy.

419. FOLSOM (FLORENCE). Love Lyrics. Dedicated to My Husband and Friend Charles Dwight Folsom. 8vo, cloth, pp. [7], 2, 64, [errata leaf].
[Boston, Mass. 1899]
Poems: "A Fiddler of the Klondike;" "Halfway to Klondike;" "Haow th' Sheriff Fell F'om Grace;" and "A Klondike Aeneid;" written at the time of the "Klondike Gold Rush." An unusual poet. Not in Sturges, McKee or Maier.

420. FRASER (D.). The Mental Flower Garden: or, An instructive and entertaining Companion for the Fair Sex. In two parts. I. A variety of entertaining and moral Dialogues, partly Original. . . . Poetic pieces, Devotional Poems, Writing Pieces, &c. II—Miscellaneous Essays . . . added interesting sketches of Female Biography. *Ornamented with appropriate Copperplates.* 12mo, original calf, pp. 299.
New York: Printed by Southwick & Hardcastle, No. 2, Wall Street. 1807
The copperplate illustrations are line engraving by Scoles, Alexander Anderson (signed copperplate and full-page wood cut) and two other unsigned copperplates. Some of the poems are original with the author.
Not in Sturges, McKee, Harris, Maier, New York Public Library or Ross's *Scottish Poets in America.*

421. FRENEAU (PHILIP). Cabinet of Monus; A choice selection of Humorous Poems from P. Pindar, Freneau . . . Humphreys . . . Hopkinson . . . &c., &c. *Embellished with six engravings.* Copy Right secured. 16mo, boards, one cover loose, a few pages stained, pp. VIII, [1] and 2 to 136.
Published by Mathew Carey, No. 122, Market Street, Philadelphia.
Printed by A. Small, 1809
Not in McKee, Harris, Maier, New York Public Library list nor PALTSITS' FINE *Freneau Bibliography.* With very fine humorous and typically American plates. Freneau's poem, "The New England Sabbath-Day Chace," is illustrated with a plate; other poems by Freneau are "Humanity and Gratitude;" "The Almanac Maker;" "Pettifogger or Fee Simple;" "Verses on the Crew of a Certain Vessell;" "Forest Beau;" "A Matrimonial Dialogue;" "College Story;" "Indian Convent."

422. [FRENEAU (PHILIP).] HEATON (NATHANIEL). The Pleasing Library, containing a selection of Humorous, Entertaining, Elegant and Instructive Pieces, in Prose and Poetry from the most celebrated writers . . . 12mo, unbound, pp. 252.
Wrentham (Mass.): Printed and sold by the Author; also sold by David Heaton, Providence, Oliver Farnoworth, Newport, Ephraim Goodale, Mendon, &c., 1801
Contains Freneau's poem, "The Indian Student or Force of Nature." Not in Sturges, McKee, etc.

423. FUGITIVE (THE): An Epic Poem in One Canto by P. Virgilius Maro. Translated by John Dryden Bags, Esq. With notes and explanations. 12mo, original printed wrappers, pp. 44 and [3].
Boston: Fetridge & Co., Publishers, 1854

A satire on the Boston Court's decision to surrender Anthony Burns the fugitive Slave. The people were so opposed to this decision that they commenced to riot, necessitating the calling of the Militia. Supposed to have been written by Virgil and transmitted through a spiritualistic medium. Not in Sturges.

424. "GAGE (HANNAH B.)." The Land by the Sunset Sea and Other Poems. Small 4to, original cloth, pp. [9], 4 to 98.
San Francisco: Philip I. Figel, Publisher, 1884

VERY SCARCE VOLUME OF CALIFORNIA VERSE. Not copyrighted. Not in Sturges, Harris, McKee or Maier.

425. GARRISON (WILLIAM LLOYD). The Nation's Shame. Sonnets . . . 12mo, wrappers, pp. 11.
Boston, Mass. [1899]

RARE. PRIVATELY PRINTED. Poems: "William McKinley;" "Aguinaldo," etc. All were written during March, April, May, June, 1899. Not in Sturges, etc.

426. GENTLEMAN'S MAGAZINE (THE), for May 1753. By Sylvanus Urban. 8vo, unbound, pp. [3], 208 to 252.
London: Printed by E. Cave [1753]

Among the Verse, is "Hor. B. I. Ode IV. Imitated. By a Friend whom Providence protects, now residing in South Carolina. Charles-Town, Mar. 26, 1753. C. W." (written to John Cordes of London). Not in Sturges, McKee, Harris, Maier or New York Public Library catalogues.

427. GIFT (THE). A Poetical Remembrancer, selected from the works of Native and Foreign authors. *Engraved frontispiece by A. Bowen, Boston.* 32mo, full old red roan, pp. 322 and Goldsmith's poems, 50pp.
Concord, N. H.: Currier and Hall and Asa McFarland, 1835

Poems by Bryant, Drake, Dana, Dinsmoor, Dr. Flint, Leggett, Longfellow, Mellen, Percival, Peabody, Prentice, Pinckney, Geo. W. Tucker, Carlos Wilcox, Richard H. Wilde, John G. Whittier, and others. Not in Sturges, Harris, McKee or Maier.

428. GOODRICH (JESSE W.). The Phrenological Organs: . . . together with The Maelstrom Wreck: The Pyramids: The Battle of Bunker Hill. A Colloquy in the Clouds: The Bridal Flounces: and some other Occasional Poems and Prose Writings of Jesse W. Goodrich [of Worcester, Mass.]. *With a Portrait.* All Prepared and Printed for the Eye, not of the Public, but of those of his kindred and friends, to whom as a memento of his kind regards this may by him be presented. 1855. 8vo, original cloth, pp. 48 and [2,].
[Worcester: Chas. Hamilton, Printer, Palladium Office, 1855]

RARE. Not in Sturges, Harris, McKee or Maier collections.

429. GOODRICH (S. G.). A Winter Wreath of Summer Flowers. *Illustrated by engravings from original designs.* 8vo, original cloth, pp. 320, gilt edges.
New York: D. Appleton and Co., MDCCCLV (1855)

In a beautiful specimen of American gilt and colored cloth binding to match the plates which are all fine colored lithographs by Champagne. Prose and Verse. Not in Sturges, McKee, Harris or Maier.

430. GOODWIN (G. FRED). A Selection of G. Fred Goodwin's Original Poems. Published by his parents for his friends. 18mo, original cloth, pp. 28.
Philadelphia: Loag, Printer . . . 1880
PRIVATELY PRINTED and rare volume of verse by the Manager of the Philadelphia Theatre. PRESENTATION COPY to J. E. Jackson. Not in Sturges, McKee, Harris, Maier, etc.

431. GOULD (ELIZABETH PORTER). Stray Pebbles from the Shores of Thought. *Portrait.* Square 18mo, cloth, pp. 220.
Boston: Press of T. O. Metcalf & Co., 1892
Pasted on front fly-leaf is a scarce leaflet poem by the same author, entitled, "On a Mule on the Nevada Trail in the Yosemite Valley, 1893." Other poems are: "To Walt Whitman;" "Lines for the Seventieth Birthday Anniversary of Walt Whitman;" "On Lake Memphremagog;" "At Pittsford, Vermont;" etc. Not in Sturges, McKee or Maier.

432. GREENE (AELLA). Rhymes of Yankee Land. 8vo, cloth, pp. 91.
Boston: Lee & Shepard, 1872
Poems: "The Yankee Westward;" "Chicago's Trial by Fire;" "The Smithville Worthies;" "The Village Schoolmaster;" etc. Not in Sturges, Maier or McKee.

433 [GRENVILLE (A. S.).] Original Poetic Effusions, Moral, Religious, and Sentimental from the pen of A. S. G. Second edition. 16mo, original boards, uncut. *Engraved half-title* and pp. 180.
Dedham: Published by John Adams, H. & W. H. Mann, Printers, 1823
Not in Sturges. FINE COPY.

434. GRIFFITH (MATTIE). Poems. Now first collected. 8vo, original cloth, pp. 167.          New York: D. Appleton & Company, MDCCLIII (1853)
Dedicated "To the Great People of Kentucky." An uncommon volume of Kentucky Verse. Not in Sturges, McKee or Maier.

PRESENTATION COPY OF A RARE VOLUME OF NEW JERSEY VERSE

435. GUEST (MOSES). Poems on Several Occasions, to which we annexed Extracts from a Journal kept by the Author while he followed the Sea, and during a Journey from New-Brunswick, in New Jersey to Montreal and Quebec. Second Edition. *Frontispiece.* 12mo, original boards, pp. 160.
Cincinnati: Looker & Reynolds, Printers, 1824
PRESENTATION COPY FROM THE AUTHOR to his niece whose neat autograph is written on title page. The artistic engraved frontispiece portrait of Lafayette with a separate leaf entitled, "An Acrostic on the General whom Ten Millions of People delight to honor," makes this volume doubly interesting, taking in account also the Sea Journal and Canadian and American Travel Journal. Poems on George Washington, "On death of Captain Peter Voorhees" (of New Brunswick, N. J.), on Gov. Livingston of New Jersey, "On the Death of Doctor Benjamin Franklin;" etc. The Verse is almost entirely of New Jersey interest.
    The Company of Militia that captured Col. Lincoln in New Jersey, 1779, was commanded by the author of the above work.

436. HALE (SARAH JOSEPH). The Poet's Offerings for 1850. [64 lines of verse by Mrs. Hale.] *Plates.* 8vo, original cloth, pp. 576.
Philadelphia: Grigg, Elliot & Co., 1850
Illustrated with 12 of Sartain's exquisite mezzotint plates and a beautiful half-title lithographed in colors. Not in Sturges, McKee, Harris or Maier.

437. HALL (A. OAKEY). The Downfall of Tammany Hall. No Fall at All not by
A. Oakey Hall. 12mo, original printed wrappers.        New York, 1871
    Characters mentioned in this poem are Tweed, Mr. Fisk and the Erie Railroad,
Gould, H. W. Beecher, Horace Greeley, Jeff Davis, Ku-Klux, Tilden, Hilton, Field,
etc. Not in Sturges, McKee, etc.

438. HANNA (HATTIE LLOYD). Poems and Hymns; also, A Few Memorials to
Bereaved Ones. 16mo, original cloth, pp. [9] and 6 to 65.
                                        Brooklyn, E. D., 1880
    SCARCE PRIVATELY PRINTED VOLUME of Brooklyn and New York local verse. Not
in Sturges, McKee, Harris or Maier.

439. HARLAN (C.—M. D.). Elflora of the Susquehanna. A Poem. *Engraved portrait of author.* 12mo, original cloth, pp. 84.
      Philadelphia: Printed for the Author, By J. B. Lippincott & Co., 1879
    The poem was written by Dr. Harlan in 1839 but not printed until 1879. PRI-
VATELY PRINTED. Not in Sturges, McKee, Harris or Maier.

440. HARLOW (WILLIAM BURT). Songs of Syracuse and Other Poems. *Portrait.*
16mo, original cloth, pp. 71 and [2] of index.
                   Syracuse, N. Y.: W. B. Harlow, 1890
    PRIVATELY PRINTED. Not in Sturges, McKee or Maier. Poems of Syracuse, N. Y.,
local interest.

441. HARRIS (ELLA STEVENS). Brown Leaves and Other Verses. Square 16mo,
original wrappers, pp. [10], 3 to 56.
      Altavista, 16 Rockledge Road, Montclair (New Jersey) [1912]
    PRIVATELY PRINTED EDITION of 100 copies. Presentation inscription, *To my
dear friend Mrs. Adele Livingston Van Cleave. From Ella Stevens Harris, February 11,
1916. Montclair, N. J.* A very scarce volume of New Jersey Verse.

442. HARRIS (JOEL CHANDLER). RUSSELL (IRWIN). Poems by Irwin Russell.
12mo, cloth, pp. XI, [2], 2 to 109.        New York: The Century Co. [1888]
    Preface is by Joel Chandler Harris. FIRST EDITION.
    Russell was a Mississippi poet born at Port Gibson, 1853, died New Orleans,
Dec. 23, 1879. Irwin was probably the first Southern Writer to appreciate the
literary possibilities of the Negro and to make use of their dialect for his verse.

443. HARTE (BRET). That Heathen Chinee and Other Humorous Poems. 12mo,
original wrappers, pp. VI, [3], 16 to 140, [2] and 20 of advts.
               London: John Camden Hotten . . . [1871]
    SCARCE. Back title worn off. This edition not in Sturges, McKee, Harris, Maier,
Ross, etc.

444. HATTERSLEY (JOHN). The Conquest of America, and Minor Poems. 16mo,
original cloth, pp. VIII, [1], 2 to 207, [1].
          London and Darlington, MDCCCXXXI (1831)
    The poem is in 3 parts, "Columbia," "Cortez" and "Pizarro." Not in Sturges, Har-
ris, McKee or Maier.

445. HARVARD COLLEGE. Carmen Saeculare. In doodle Yankee cantandum. 8vo,
3 page leaflet.        [Harvard College, 1836]
    RARE. *See* Companion piece under Broadsides, Harvard College, 1836. Not in
Sturges, etc.

446. HARVARD VERSE. Verses from the Harvard Advocate. (First Series), pp. XIII, [4] and 2 to 254—Charles W. Seaver, Cambridge, 1876; (Second Series) New Verses from the Harvard Advocate, 1876–1886. Reprinted for the Use of Later Undergraduates. pp. XIV, [2], 3 to 192, [1]. Privately printed by Kilbourne Tompkins, New York [1886]; (Third Series) Verses from the Harvard Advocate. Third Series, 1886–1906. pp. XIII, [3] and 3 to 214. Cambridge. The Harvard Advocate, 1906. Together, 3 vols. 8vo, cloth. Cambridge and New York, 1876–1906

Sets like above are not easy to gather. Not in Sturges, McKee, Harris or Maier catalogues.

447. HAY (JOHN). Jim Bludso of the Prairie Belle and Little Breeches. *Illustrated by Eytinge.* 12mo, original printed wrappers, faded, pp. 23.
Boston: James R. Osgood & Co., 1871
FIRST EDITION.

448. HEADY (MORRISON). The Double Night and Other Poems. 8vo, cloth, pp. 316.
Courier-Journal Job Printing Co., Louisville, Kentucky [1901]

These poems are the work of a man both blind and deaf. He was born in Spencer County, Kentucky, 1829. Not in Sturges.

449. HELMUTH (JUSTUS HEINRICH CHRISTIAN). Die erlaubte Klage über den Abschied treuer Knechte Gottes. Eine Gedaechtnisspredigt auf den Seligen Tod Seiner Hochwürden des Herrn D. Heinrich Melchior Mühlenberg's, redlichen ersten Lehrers der St. Michaelis- und Zions-Gemeinde in Philadelphia, gehalten in der Zions-Kirche, den 21. October 1787, von Just. Heinrich Christian Helmuth, Prediger allhier. [The first title which takes the place of a half-title is here and begins] Denkmal der Liebe und Achtung, [etc., etc. with same imprint and date]. *Portrait.* 8vo.
Philadelphia: Gedruckt bey Melchior Steiner, 1788

Not in Sturges, etc.
Contains rare copper-engraved portrait of Dr. Mühlenberg. The poems and songs, 8 in number, contain over 420 lines of verse on the death of Dr. Mühlenberg. Evans gives complete title but does not state the location of any copy of the above item. Seidensticker locates a copy in the German Society collections. Otherwise no copy of this Memorial Sermon in Prose and Verse is located. Gives an account also of the chief events in the life of Dr. Mühlenberg, the Patriarch of the Lutheran Church in America. See under Broadsides, No. 127.

450. HERCKMANS (ELIAS). Der Zee-Vaert Lof Handelende vande gedonckwaerdighste Zee vaerden met de daeraenklevende op en onderganghen der voornaemste Heerrschappyen der gantscher Wereld: Zedert haere beginselen tot op den dagh van huyden. Door E. Herckmans. *Engraved title and curious illustrations* Folio, vellum. Amsterdam, 1634

Sabin, 31476. "The author of this excessively curious and rare work was Vice-Admiral of the celebrated expedition of the Dutch in 1643 under Admiral Hendrick Brouwer, against the Spaniards of Chile. . . . Zee-Vaert Lof is an elaborate poem in six books in honor of navigation. All the celebrated voyages of the world to 1632 are recorded in chronological order. The voyages of discovery, leading up to the discovery of America, are mentioned with considerable detail, and after Columbus are recorded most of the voyages both to the east and to the west, especially the expeditions of the Dutch navigators. The voyages to the north are all mentioned in the text, and notes. The volume is beautifully illustrated by an engraved title and eighteen exquisite etchings in the text. The one at the beginning of the third book bears the mark of Rembrandt, with the date 1633." (Stevens.)

451. HEWES (GEORGE WHITFIELD). Ballads of the War. 8vo, original cloth, pp. 147.
New-York: Carleton, Publisher,130 Canal St., MDCCCLXII (1862)
Poems:—"Ballad of Everard Gray;" "A Brother in the Rebel Army;" "To the
Hero of Missouri;" "Love of the Wounded Zouave;" "Lament from Fort Lafayette;"
"Grave Digger of Manassas;" etc. Not in Sturges, McKee, Harris or Maier.

452. HILL (BENJAMIN DIONYSIUS). Poems: Devotional and Occasional. 12mo,
original cloth, pp. [2] and 142.
New York: The Catholic Publication Society, 9 Warren Street.    1877
Catholic poems written by a Catholic Priest. SCARCE. Not in Sturges, McKee,
Harris or Maier.

453. HITT (ADRIAN). The Grant Poem, containing Grant's Public Career, and
Private Life from the Cradle to the Grave.  General Grant, what a Volume
in a name, an Army in a Man. . . . *Designed, illustrated and Engraved by the
Author.* 8vo, cloth, pp. 381.    New York: Nassau Publishing Co., 1886
This book needs no introduction; it's the poetic side of a "Bloody Ruction." Not
in Sturges, McKee, Harris or Maier.

454. HOLLAND (J. G.). Kathrina.  Her Life and Mine in a Poem. *Illustrations by
W. J. Hennessy, and C. C. Griswold. Engraved by W. J. Linton.* Tall 8vo,
original green gilt cloth, pp. XII, [1], 281, [1], gilt edges.
New York: Charles Scribner & Company, MDCCCLXIX (1869)
FINE LARGE PAPER COPY, the first edition with illustrations. Not in Sturges,
McKee, Harris or Maier.

455. HORTON (MARY L.). Poetical and Prose Compositions. 18mo, boards, roan
back, pp. [5], 11 to 111, [2] and 2 to 88.
Salem: W. & S. B. Ives.  Essex Street.   1832
See Perley's *Poets of Essex Co.* [Mass.] for an extended account of this poet.
Not in Sturges, McKee, Maier.

456. HOWELLS (WILLIAM DEAN).  No Love Lost.  A Romance of Travel. *Illustra-
tions.* Small 4to, original cloth, pp. 58, gilt edges.
New York: G. P. Putnam & Son, 1869
Scarce poem by Howells. FIRST EDITION.

457. [HOWLAND (HENRY R.).] Voices of the Glen. *Illustrations.* Small 4to, cloth,
pp. VII, [5], 2 to 95, [4].    New York. The Knickerbocker Press. [1911]
PRESENTATION COPY. Poems on "Glen Iris" which embraces the Upper and
Middle Falls of the Upper Genesee River. A scarce volume of verse by Howland
and other authors, written 1860 to 1910 inclusive. Second and COMPLETE EDITION.
Not in Sturges.

458. HOYT (REV. R.).  Sketches—No. I.  Julia, an Autumnal Tale. 8vo, sewed,
pp. 8.    [New York] Spalding & Shepard [1847]
VERY SCARCE.  Not in Sturges, McKee or Maier. This note also applies to the
following 7 lots.  Note change of printer in last two lots.  These are the original
"Sketches" issued in pamphlet form—later issued in cloth-bound book-form in 1852–
59 under title of "Sketches of Life and Landscape."
Hoyt, while a native of New York City, passed his earlier years in Long Island;
his later years were spent in his home at Fort Lee, New Jersey.

459. HOYT (REV. R.).  Sketches—No. II.  Edward Bell, A rural sketch of May.
8vo, sewed, pp. 10.    [New York] Spalding & Shepard [1847]
Not in Sturges, etc.

460. HOYT (REV. R.). Sketches—No. III. Snow, A rural sketch of Winter. 8vo, sewed, pp. 10. [New York] Spalding & Shepard [1847]
Not in Sturges, etc.

461. HOYT (REV. R.). Sketches—No. IV. The World-Sale, A Moral Sketch. 8vo, sewed, pp. 10. [New York] Spalding & Shepard [1847]
Not in Sturges, etc.

462. HOYT (REV. R.). Sketches,—No. V. Old. [Poem of an Old Pilgrim musing on his past life.] 8vo, sewed, pp. 10.
[New York] Spalding & Shepard, 189½ Broadway, 1847
SCARCE. Fourth edition, date at end. Not in Sturges, etc.

463. HOYT (REV. R.). Sketches—No. VI. New, A portraiture of Discontent. 8vo, sewed, pp. 10. [New York] Spalding & Shepard [1847]
Not in Sturges, etc.

464. HOYT (REV. R.). Sketches—No. VII. Rain, A Rural Summer Reminiscence. 8vo, sewed, pp. 10. New York: G. Shepard [1848]
Not in Sturges, etc.

465. HOYT (REV. R.). Sketches—No. VIII. Outalissa, A Tradition of Seneca Lake. 8vo. sewed, pp. [10].
New York: C. Shepard, 191 Broadway, Price Sixpence [1848]
An Indian Legend of Lake Seneca, Geneva, N. Y. Not in Sturges, McKee or Maier catalogues.

466. HUBBARD (JOHN). The American Reader, Containing A Selection of Narrations, Harangues, Addresses, Orations, Dialogues, Odes, Hymns, Poems, &c. Designed for the use of Schools: Together with a short introduction. Second Edition. Published According to Act of Congress. 12mo, calf, pp. 215 and [1].
Walpole, N. H. Printed for Thomas & Thomas, Proprietors of the work, by G. W. Nichols, and sold wholesale and retail at the Walpole Bookstore. 1807
Nice specimen of an Early American Reader, with American verse. Not in Sturges, etc.

467. HULL (JOSEPH—of Oswego, N. Y.). What I Know Of Farming: Founded on the experience of Horace Greeley. *Illustrated by the Author.* 12mo, original printed wrappers, 14 leaves, printed on one side only. No place, no date
Not known to Henschel; not in Sturges, McKee or Maier collections. Anti-Greeley poem.

468. HYLTON (DR. J. DUNBAR). Above the Grave of John Odenswinge, A Cosmopolite. *Portrait.* 8vo, cloth covers, back gone, pp. 80.
New York: Howard Challen, 744 Broadway, and the Author, Palmyra, N. J. 1884
By Dr. Hylton of Palmyra, New Jersey. The other poems included are:—"My Jersey Girl;" "Battle of the Dogs and Cats;" "My Yankee Maid" (the original version); etc. Not in Sturges, McKee, Harris or Maier.

469. HYLTON (DR. J. DUNBAR). The Praesidicide and Battle of Antietam. Second Edition. 8vo, unbound, pp. 148.        New York: Howard Challen, 1884

> Poem on J. Wilkes Booth, the murderer of Abraham Lincoln. By the Author of "Voices from the Rocky Mountains," a Palmyra, New Jersey, Poet. Not in Sturges, Harris or Maier, and *this edition* not in McKee.

470. INKERMAN. [Poem.] By a Guardsman. Baltimore, 1855. 8vo, sewed, pp. 15.
New York: Edward Dunigan & Brother, 1856

> Not in Sturges, etc.

471. IRIS (SCHARMEL). Lyrics of a Lad. With a preface by Maurice Francis Egan. *Portrait.* 8vo, boards, uncut edges, pp. 77, [1].
Chicago: Ralph Fletcher Seymour Co., 1914

> FIRST EDITION. PRESENTATION COPY to *Mr. Ed. J. Wheeler with the sincere appreciation of the author, Scharmel Iris.*

472. [JOHN (PILGRIM).] Our Soldier's Armour of Strength [2 lines of verse]. A Brief Course of Non-Sectarian Devotional Exercises, Applied Scripture Quotations, Proverbs, and Aphorisms, Extracts, Poetical Contributions and Hymns; specially adapted to the Present Calamitous Times of Rebellion and Civil War, by Pilgrim John. *Portrait of Gen. Lyon.* 8vo, original cloth, pp. 90.
Brooklyn, E. D.  Published and Sold by D. S. Holmes, 67 Fourth-Street, 1862

> Dedicated to Abraham Lincoln. Preface dated Feb. 22, 1862, Long Island. The author was a well-known playwright. Not in Sturges, McKee or Maier.

473. JOHNSON (ANNIE E.). Songs from Nahant. I dedicate these little songs affectionately to my children. 8vo, original cloth, 97 unnumbered pages.
Lynn, Mass.: Press of G. H. & W. A. Nichols, 1892

> Not in Sturges, McKee or Maier.

474. JOHNSON (REV. N. EMMONS). The Sacred Seal; or, The Wanderer Restored, A Poem. *Frontispiece.* 8vo, original cloth, pp. 80.
New York: John S. Taylor & Co., 1843

> Poem on the son of an old New England family who, breaking away from the religious life of his forefathers, became a wanderer around the world.

475. [JOHNSON (JUDGE).] The Chemung and its Tributaries [a Poem]. 16mo, original printed wrappers, pp. 25.        [Corning, N. Y., 1872?]

> RARE PRIVATELY PRINTED volume of Upstate New York Verse. PRESENTATION COPY from Mrs. Maynard, daughter of Judge Johnson. Not in Sturges, Harris, McKee, Maier, etc.

476. JOHNSON (E. PAULINE). The White Wampum, by E. Pauline Johnson. Tekahionwake. 8vo, original cloth, uncut edges, pp. VIII, 88, 16.
London: John Lane, 1895

> FIRST EDITION. FINE COPY, UNCUT. The authoress was called "Tekahionwake" by the Indians of Canada. Poems: "Ojistoh;" "The Pilot of the Plains;" "The Cattle Thief;" etc. Not in Sturges, McKee or Maier.

477. JOHNSTON (WILLIAM PRESTON). My Garden Walk. 8vo, original cloth, pp. 183.        No place [Hansell & Bro., 1895]

[ *Continued*

PRIVATELY PRINTED, PRESENTATION COPY. One of the Poems, "The Texas Mother's Lament," written in 1854, relates to an occurrence similar to one which also took place in Texas in 1868, the murder of a mother and 4 little children by the Savages in Wise County, Northern Texas. The oldest boy, 12 years of age, a "Crack Shooter," killed 7 of the Indians before his own death. Not in Sturges, McKee or Maier.

478. JUDSON (EMILY). An Olio of Domestic Verse. 8vo, original cloth, pp. 235 and [4]. New York: Published by Lewis Colby, 1852

Preface dated Hamilton, N. Y. The authoress became a popular writer under the pseudonym of "Fanny Forrester." Not in Sturges, McKee or Maier.

479. KEESE (JOHN). The Opal: A Pure Gift for the Holydays. MDCCCXLVII. *With illustrations by Chapman.* 8vo, original cloth, pp. 304. New York: J. C. Riker, 1847

Among the Mezzotint engravings are 3 PRINTED IN COLORS, which I believe to be the only ones ever done for an annual in America. Among the authors are Richard Grant White, Mrs. Osgood, Mrs. E. Oakes Smith, C. F. Hoffman, J. M. Legare, H. W. Longfellow ("Birds of Passage"), "Dirge," by J. W. Wilde, etc. Not in Sturges, McKee, Harris or Maier.

480. KENNEDY (CRAMMOND). Corn in the Blade. Poems, and Thoughts in Prose. With an introduction by C. B. Conant. *Portrait of Author.* 8vo, original cloth, pp. 213. New York: Derby & Jackson, 498 Broadway, 1860

Not in Sturges, McKee or Maier. A great many of the poems in the above volume were written by the author when only 15 years of age.

481. KING (PATRICK MARTIN). Verses. Small 4to, full morocco, rubbed, pp. 112. San Francisco, 1890

A rare volume of PRIVATELY PRINTED VERSE BY A CALIFORNIA AUTHOR. Not in Sturges, McKee, Maier, etc.

482. LAIGHTON (ALBERT). Poems. *Title printed in red and black.* 12mo, original cloth, pp. 135.
Boston: Brown, Taggard & Chase. Portsmouth: Joseph Hiller Foster, 1859

Portsmouth, New Hampshire, Poet. The volume ends with "A Sonnet to J. G. W." [Whittier]. Not in Sturges, McKee or Maier.

483. LAWRENCE (ISAAC). Shadows of the Metropolis [New York]. 8vo, original printed wrappers, pp. 8. New York: Printed by R. Craighead, 1859

Not in Sturges, McKee or Maier. See also under American Plays.

484. LAZARUS (EMMA). Admetus and Other Poems. 8vo, new cloth, pp. 230. New York: Hurd and Houghton, 1871

Not in Sturges, McKee or Harris.

485. LAZARUS (EMMA). Poems and Translations. Written between the ages of Fourteen and Sixteen. 8vo, original cloth, pp. VII, [2] and 2 to 207. New York: Printed for Private Circulation, 1866

FINE COPY, with copyrighted slip pasted in. This author's first publication. Not in McKee or Harris, both not listing even one title by this author. The above is the only title listed in Sturges, while this collection has four. (See under American Plays for the fourth item.)

486. LAZARUS (EMMA). The Poems of. . . In two volumes. Narrative, Lyric and Dramatic. 2 vols., small 8vo, cloth. Vol. I: pp. v, [2] and 2 to 342; Vol. II: pp. 5, [2], 2 to 257.
Boston and New York: Houghton, Mifflin and Company, 1889
Not in Sturges, McKee or Harris.

487. LEE (ARTHUR T.). Army Ballads and Other Poems by Arthur T. Lee, U. S. A. *With illustrations designed by the Author.* 12mo, original cloth, pp. 160.
No place, 1871
PRIVATELY PRINTED. DEDICATED to "Gen. W. T. Sherman and to my comrades of many a joyous hour stolen from the vicissitudes of Frontier Life." Poems: "The Express Rider;" "Drummer Boy;" "Down in Sweet Wyoming Vale;" "Oh! I'm Sick of this War;" "On the Wild, Wide Mississippi;" "Mule's Lament;" "When the Mexicans were Flying;" etc. On pp. 148 to 150 is "A Dramatic Sketch." Not in Sturges, McKee, Harris or Maier.

488. LEEDOM (B. J.). The Voyage to Harlem [New York], thirty years ago, And Other Poems. *Illustrated.* 8vo, cloth, pp. 111.
Philadelphia: T. Ellwood Zell, 1867
Not in Sturges. Poem on Death of McDonald Clarke, Mexican War, On the Reception of Henry Clay by the Ladies of Philadelphia, First Prayer in Congress, Niagara from Goat Island, Oakland, near Hempstead, Long Island, etc.

489. LELAND (CHARLES G.). Hans Breitmann's Party. With Other Ballads. 8vo, original printed wrappers, pp. 32.
Philadelphia: T. B. Peterson & Brothers [1868]
FIRST EDITION, WITH 32 PAGES. Not in Sturges.

490. LELAND (CHARLES G.). Hans Breitmann's Party. With Other Ballads. New and Enlarged Edition. 8vo, original printed wrappers, pp. 48.
Philadelphia: T. B. Peterson & Brothers [1869]
The 48-page edition. Not in Sturges or McKee.

491. LELAND (CHARLES G.). Hans Breitmann's Ballads. Complete in One Volume. 8vo, original cloth, pp. 118.
Philadelphia: T. B. Peterson & Brothers [1869]
The 118-page edition. FIRST EDITION, not in Sturges, McKee or Harris.

492. LELAND (CHARLES G.). Hans Breitmann's Ballads. New, Enlarged and Complete Edition. 8vo, original cloth, pp. 168.
Philadelphia: T. B. Peterson & Brothers [1870]
The 168-page edition. FIRST ENLARGED EDITION, not in Sturges, McKee or Harris.

493. LELAND (CHARLES G.). Hans Breitmann About Town. And Other New Ballads. Second Series of the Breitmann Ballads. 8vo, unbound, pp. 62 and blank leaf.
Philadelphia: T. B. Peterson & Brothers [1869]
FIRST EDITION. Not in Sturges.

494. LELAND (CHARLES G.). Hans Breitmann In Church. With Other New Ballads. Third Series of the Breitmann Ballads. 8vo, original printed wrappers, pp. 8, [1] and 108 to 154.
Philadelphia: T. B. Peterson & Brothers [1870]
FIRST EDITION, UNCUT AND UNOPENED COPY. Not in Sturges, Harris or McKee.

495. LELAND (CHARLES G.). Hans Breitmann in Politics. A Humorous Poem. *Frontispiece.* 8vo, original printed wrappers, pp. 13.

Philadelphia: J. B. Lippincott & Co., 1869

FIRST EDITION, not in Sturges or McKee.


496. LELAND (CHARLES G.). Johnnykin and the Goblins. *Illustrated by the Author.* 8vo, original cloth, pp. 212, [2].

New York: Macmillan & Co., 1876. All rights reserved

FIRST EDITION. VERY SCARCE, written in prose and verse. Not in Sturges, McKee, Harris or Maier.


497. LELAND (CHARLES G.). The Poetry and Mystery of Dreams. [4 lines from Chaucer.] 8vo, original cloth, pp. 271, [16 page catalogue].

Philadelphia: Published by E. H. Butler & Co., MDCCCLVI (1856)

Not in Sturges or McKee. Bookplates of James Olcott Brown and Francis Clifford Prescott in front.


498. [LELAND (CHARLES G.).] United States Service Magazine. Vol. I. 8vo, cloth, pp. iv, [1], 668.

New York: Charles B. Richardson, 441 Broadway, 1865

Contains a fine 19-page article by Leland, entitled, "War Songs and their influence in History." With other verse by Baker, Washburne, MacKellar and Lieut. Gibson. VERY SCARCE.
Not in Sturges, McKee, Harris or Maier.


499. LEWIS (ALONZO), The Poems of. . . . Ninth edition. 32mo, original cloth, pp. 127, [1].

Boston: B. B. Mussey & Co., 1851

By the "Lynn Bard," "Sassacus" (poem on the last great Sachem of the Pequod Indians); "Last of the Sagus Tribe;" "Sea Shells" (poem on Nahant); also other Nahant Poems; "The Cloud Ship" (poem on a ship lost in New Haven Bay in 1646, in 1648 the same ship appeared and vanished like an apparition); etc. This edition not in Sturges, Harris, McKee or Maier.


500. LIFE AND TIMES OF SAM. Written by Himself. 8vo, unbound, pp. 32, corners water-stained.

Claremont, N. H.: Tracy and Sanford, 1855

Very scarce political poem, partly Anti-President Pierce and Anti-Irish and Catholic. The Author in his poem calls the "Nebraska Bill," "Niggerbraskal bill." Not in Sturges and other lists consulted.


501. LIGHT (GEORGE W.). Keep Cool, Go Ahead, and a Few Other Poems. 16mo, original cloth, pp. 35. Boston: Published by the Author, 3 Cornhill, 1851

Not in Sturges, McKee or Maier collections.


FIRST REGULAR VOLUME OF VERSE PRINTED IN MAINE (WRITTEN BY MAINE'S THIRD GOVERNOR)

502. [LINCOLN (ENOCH).] The Village; A Poem with an appendix. 16mo, original boards (loose), paper title-label on back, pp. 180.

Portland (Maine): Published by Edward Little and Co.
C. Norris & Co., printers, 1816

Issued anonymously by the author, who was the fourth son of Levi Lincoln of Mass. A poem of over 2000 lines descriptive of the Scenery of the Saco Valley, and of Rural Life and characters in Maine.

503. [Lincoln (Abraham).] Snider (Denton J.). Lincoln in the Black Hawk War. An Epos of the Northwest. 8vo, cloth, leather title-label, pp. 375.
St. Louis, Mo.: Sigma Publishing Co., no date
First volume of the Tetralogy.

504. [Lincoln (Abraham).] Snider (Denton J.). Lincoln and Ann Rutledge. An Idyllic Epos of the Early North-West. 8vo, cloth, pp. 350.
St. Louis: Sigma Publishing Co. [1912]
Second volume of the Tetralogy.

505. [Lincoln (Abraham).] Snider (Denton J.). Lincoln in the White House. A dramatic Epos of the Civil War. 8vo, cloth, pp. 404 and [1].
St. Louis, Mo.: Sigma Publshing Co., no date
Third volume of the Tetralogy.

506. [Lincoln (Abraham).] Snider (Denton J.). Lincoln at Richmond. A dramatic Epos of the Civil War. 8vo, cloth, pp. 388.
St. Louis, Mo.: Sigma Publishing Co. [1914]
Fourth volume of the Tetralogy.

507. [Lincoln (Abraham).] Snider (Denton J.). Abraham Lincoln. An interpretation in Biography. 8vo, cloth, pp. 574.
St. Louis, Mo.: Sigma Publishing Co., [1908]
The above is a necessary companion to the Tetralogy, a national Epos in four separate volumes corresponding to the chief epochs of Lincoln's career, and setting forth especially his inner life and its transformations along with the outer events of his time.

508. Little (Sophia L.). The Last Days of Jesus. 12mo, original printed wrappers, pp. 60.      Pawtucket, R. I.: Printed for the Author, 1841
The Very Scarce First Edition. Sturges had the 1841 and Harris had the 1877 edition only, not in McKee or Maier. The authoress was a daughter of Hon. Asa Robbins of Newport. She married Wm. Little, Jr., of Boston.

RARE VOLUME OF COLONIAL AMERICAN VERSE BY WILLIAM LIVINGSTON, GOVERNOR OF NEW JERSEY, 1776–1790, AND HEAD GRADUATE, YALE COLLEGE, 1741

509. [Livingston (William).] Philosophic Solitude: or, The Choice of A Rural Life: A Poem. By a Gentleman educated at Yale College. [2 lines of Latin.] 8vo, sewed, pp. 46, Edges Uncut.
New-York: Printed, MDCCXLVII. Boston: Reprinted and Sold by B. Mecom, at the New Printing-Office, near the Town-House, 1762
Not in Sturges, Harris, McKee, Maier or New York Public Library collections. Name on title and half-title, small repair on margin of page 20, and small hole repaired on page 21 affecting 2 words of text. Some pages time discolored. This is the Very Rare Second Edition, printed by Benjamin Franklin's Nephew and has the Edges Uncut.
The author was only 24 years of age when he wrote this poem. The poem itself is not a mere literary exercise, stiff and conventional, but springs from a genuinely lyric impulse.

510. [Livingston (William).] Moore (J. Hamilton). The Young Gentleman and Lady's Monitor, and English Teacher's Assistant: Being a Collection of Select pieces from our Best Modern Writers. [14 more lines of title.] 16mo, old calf, pp. vi, [1], 2 to 406 and [8].

[Continued

[No. 510. LIVINGSTON (WILLIAM)—*Continued*]

New-York: Printed and Sold by William Durell, at his Book-Store and Printing Office, No. 19, Queen Street, M,DCC,XCII (1792)

Pages 325 to 342 inclusive contain:—"Choice of a Rural Life: A Poem. Written by W. L. Esq. Gov. of N. J." This edition not listed in the New York Public Library list, Sturges, McKee or elsewhere.

511. LOCKE (JANE E.).  Boston: A Poem.  16mo, original printed wrappers, pp. 46 and errata leaf.      Boston: Wm. Crosby and H. P. Nichols . . . 1846

Second edition.  Not in Sturges, McKee, Harris or Maier catalogues.

512. LOEW'S BRIDGE, A Broadway Idyl.  *Illustrations.*  Square 16mo, original cloth, pp. 78.                    New York: M. Doolady, Publisher, 1867

A poem of New York Life in 1866, on the Police, Wall Street, Mayor Hoffman, Fernando Wood, Wm. Cullen Bryant and the "Evening Post," Horace Greeley, Maggie Mitchell (the Actress), Joe Jefferson, Mrs. Lander, Dr. Foote (of "Medical Common Sense" fame), etc.  Not in Sturges, McKee, Harris or Maier.

513. [LOCKWOOD (JOHN).]  Address and Poem ["Palermo," A Broken Ballad by John Lockwood, Class of 1848] before The Association of the Alumni of Columbia.  8vo, original printed wrappers, pp. [7], 6 to 44 and 36 and [1].
New York: Published by the Association, 1861

The poem by Lockwood is the 1860 Class Poem, no copy of the manuscript for the 1861 poem being obtainable.  Not in Sturges, McKee or Maier.

514. LOGAN (ALGERNON SYDNEY).  The Mirror of a Mind.  A Poem.  Square 8vo, original cloth, pp. 116.
New York: Published for the Author by G. P. Putnam's Sons, 1875

PRIVATELY PRINTED.  Not in Sturges, McKee, Harris or Maier.

## A LONGFELLOW DISCOVERY! THE REAL FIRST EDITION OF "EXCELSIOR"

515. LONGFELLOW (HENRY W.).  Excelsior, Words by Henry W. Longfellow, Music Composed and Sung by the Hutchinson Family.  This poem represents the continued aspirations of Genius.  Its Motto "Excelsior" (still higher) is a word in an unknown tongue.  Disregarding the every day comforts of life, the allurements of love, and the warnings of experience, it presses forward on its solitary path.  Even in death it holds fast its device and a voice from the air proclaims the progress of the Soul in a higher sphere.  Large 4to, wrappers, pp. 7 including wrappers.
New York: Firth & Hall, 1843

THIS IS THE REAL FIRST SEPARATE EDITION OF LONGFELLOW'S POEM "EXCELSIOR," preceding the pirated "Excelsior Life Insurance Company's" edition (1872) by 29 years.  Lacking in all the notable first edition collections sold at auction.  The front wrapper has portraits of the Hutchinson Family.  Little foxed and top margins water-stained.

Copyright note reads: Entered according to Act of Congress, A.D. 1843 by Firth & Hall, in the Clerk's Office of the District Court of the Southn. Dist. of New York.

516. LONGFELLOW (HENRY W.).  Poems on Slavery.  Second edition.  12mo, new silk cloth, pp. 31 and 8-page catalogue.
Cambridge: Published by John Owen, MDCCCXLII (1842)

Printed same year as first edition.  AN UNCUT AND UNOPENED COPY, extremely rare in such condition, and very hard to duplicate.

517. [LONGFELLOW (HENRY W.).] Chimasia: A Reply to Longfellow's Theologian; and Other Poems by Orthos. 8vo, original cloth, pp. 96.
Philadelphia: J. B. Lippincott & Co., 715 and 717 Market Street, 1864
Not in Sturges, McKee or Maier. FINE COPY.

518. LOSKIEL (GEORGE HENRY). Extempore on a Wagon; A Metrical Narrative of a Journey from Bethlehem, Pa., to the Indian Town of Goshen, Ohio, in the Autumn of 1803. Translated with notes by J. Max Hark. *Portrait.* 8vo, original cloth, pp. 45, [1].
Lancaster, Pa.: Published by Samuel H. Zahn & Co., 1887
Only 200 copies were printed. Not in McKee, Maier or New York Public Library catalogues.

519. LOUD (MRS. M. ST. LEON). Wayside Flowers: A Collection of Poems. *Engraved portrait of the Authoress.* 8vo, original cloth, pp. xii, [1], 2 to 276. (Stamp on title.)    Boston: Ticknor, Reed and Fields, MDCCCLI (1851)
The preface is signed P. B. [Park Benjamin], Newport, R. I. Sept. 17, 1850. The authoress lived quite a while in the South. Poems:—"The Seminole's Death;" "A Tale of Florida;" "The Dying Buffalo;" "Indian Legend of a Spring in Florida;" "Destruction of the Pulaski" (Steamer lost on her passage from Charleston, South Carolina, to New York); etc. Not in Sturges, McKee or Maier.

520. [LOW (WALTER).] Palmetto Pictures. 12mo, original cloth, pp. 67.
New York: Walter Low, 1863
A scarce volume of Southern verse, dedicated to the author's Class in Yale, '57. Not in Sturges, McKee or Maier. The author was evidently from Beaufort, South Carolina, judging from some of his War Verse.

521. [LOWE (MRS. C.).] The Olive and the Pine. 8vo, original cloth, pp. vii, [3], 4 to 156 and errata leaf.    Boston: Crosby, Nichols, and Co., 1859
Part II, pages 71 to 131 inclusive, are poems on New England. Not in Sturges, McKee or Maier. A Keene, N. H., author.

522. [LUNT (GEORGE).] Requiem. Dedicated to the memory of the slain in battle. *Printed in colors.* 4to, cloth, 6 ll., gilt edges.    [Boston, 1862]
RARE. PRIVATELY PRINTED.

523. LYONS (REV. JAMES GILBORNE). Christian Songs, Translations, and Other Poems. 8vo, cloth, pp. 157.    Philadelphia: Smith, English & Co., 1861
West Haverford, Penna., author. Not in Sturges, McKee, Harris or Maier.

524. McCAFFERY (MICHAEL J. A.). The Siege of Spoleto; A Camp-Tale of Arlington Heights. 12mo, original cloth, pp. 90, [6].
New York: P. O'Shea, 104 Bleecker St., 1864
FINE COPY OF THIS SCARCE WORK by a Catholic Irishman, relates to the Sixtyninth Regt., N. Y. Not in Sturges, Harris or Maier.

525. McCAFFERY (MICHAEL J. A.). The Worst Boy in the School. *With illustrations.* 8vo, cloth, pp. 59.
New York: G. W. Dillingham Co., MDCCCXCVII (1897)
PRESENTATION COPY TO *Edward C. Boardman, Esq., with compliments of the author June 12, 1900.* By the author of the "Siege of Spoleto" a scarce Civil War poem.

526. McCALLUM (D. C.). The Water Mill; and Other Poems. 16mo, original cloth, pp. 57 and [6].          Brooklyn, N. Y.: Privately Printed, 1870
    PRIVATELY PRINTED PRESENTATION COPY. *To Robert Davis, Esq., by his friend D. C. McCallum, New York, Nov. 14th, 1872.* Poem: "By Request of Sagamore Lodge, Free & Ancient Masons;" "Lost Forevermore" (on style of Poe's Raven); "Creed of Life;" "Rainy Day;" etc. Not in Sturges, McKee, Harris or Maier.

527. McDONALD (A. J.—Editor). The Rainbow, 1847. *Engraved plates.* 8vo, original leather, pp. 272.  Albany: A. L. Harrison, MDCCCXLVII (1847)
    Although faded, the binding is still a fine specimen of early American ornamental work in gilt and inlays of leathers of different colors.
    Authors are listed by States as follows: Virginia (Judge Tucker); New York (Sprague, Street, Hatch, Tuckerman, etc.); Massachusetts (Gleason, Gould, Field); New Jersey (Stacy G. Potts); Delaware (Wm. Penn Chandler); Maine (Miss Gardner); Maryland (Park Benjamin); and 12 other States.

528. M'JILTON (J. N.). Poems. 8vo, original cloth, pp. 360.
                              Boston: Otis Broaders & Co., 1840
    PRESENTATION COPY TO *Eleazer Parmly, M.D. With the respects of the Author.* Baltimore poet and verse. The first poem is, "Triumph of Liberty, pronounced before the associated Literary and Scientific Societies of Baltimore, Fourth of July, 1838." This volume was printed in Baltimore, although having Boston imprint. Not in Sturges, McKee or Maier.


UNKNOWN GERMAN-AMERICAN POETICAL DIALOGUE

529. [MACK (VALENTINE).] Ein Gespräch zwischen einem Pilger und Bürger, Auf ihrer Reise nach und in der Ewigkeit. Welchem noch hinzugefüst ist, ein Gespräch das der Tod mit Beiden gehalten. [10-line quotation from Esaia, 57, 2, and Cap. 5, 3.45.] 18mo, original wrappers, pp. 49.
              Chestnuthill [Phila., Pa.]: Gedruckt bey Samuel Saur, 1792
    No copy located by Seidensticker in his *History of German American Printing.* Evans copied his title from Seidensticker and also locates no copy. Both *by error* give 72 pp. but this copy is COMPLETE with 49 pages as it finishes with the word, "Ende." Not in Sturges or elsewhere.

530. MALONEY (MARY T.). The Legend of Nonnenwerth, and Other Poems. 16mo, original cloth, pp. 126.          San Jose, Cal., J. J. Owen, Printer, 1876
    Not in Sturges, McKee, Harris or Maier. SCARCE VOLUME OF A CALIFORNIA AUTHOR AND IMPRINT.

531. MARCH (DANIEL). Yankee Land and The Yankee. 8vo, original cloth, pp. 33.
              Hartford: Printed by Case, Tiffany and Burnham, 1840.
    Delivered before the Centennial of the Connecticut Historical Society. Not in Sturges.

532. [MARIE (PETER).] Sunny Sue. A Vision of Fairy Land. 8vo, original wrappers, pp. [7] and VI to XVII. [New York: Hall, Clayton & Co. Printers, 189–?]
    PRIVATELY PRINTED with following inscription in author's autograph: *Presented to Miss Upton as a slight souvenir of an agreeable trip across the Atlantic, made in her company, on board the Steamship "America," by the author, P. Marie. Left Boston 21st May, arrived at Liverpool, 1st June.* Not in Sturges, McKee, Harris, Maier, etc.

533. MARSH (MRS. GEORGE P.). Wolfe of the Knoll, and Other Poems. 8vo, cloth, pp. 327 (library stamp on title but a fine copy).
                              New York: Charles Scribner, 1860
    Vermont Poetess, wife of Prof. Marsh. Not in Sturges, McKee or Maier.

534. MARSHALL (WILLIAM E.). Cuba: Queen of the Antilles. By William Edgar Marshall. 12mo, original wrappers, sewed, pp. 17.

New York: Issued by the Author, 1897

By the noted engraver and painter. SCARCE PRIVATELY PRINTED ITEM, not in Sturges, McKee, Maier, etc.

535. [MATHEWS (CORNELIUS).] Wakondah; The Master of Life. A Poem. 8vo, original gilt decorated boards, paper title-label, cover loose, pp. 24.

New York: George L. Curry. MDCCCXLI (1841)

Splendid and unusual poem, based on the superstitious feeling of the Indians regarding the Chippewyan or Rocky Mountains. This item was printed at St. Thomas' Hall Press, Flushing, Long Island, a scarce Long Island imprint. Not in Harris catalogue.

536. MATTHEWS (BRANDER). Poems of American Patriotism, Chosen by Brander Matthews. 8vo, cloth, pp. xiii, [2], 2 to 285.

New York: Charles Scribner's Sons, 1882

A fine gathering of Patriotic Verse by our best poets. Not in Sturges, McKee, Harris or Maier.

537. MELMOTH (SYDNEY). The Confessions of Cuthburt, A Ballad. Bunker Hill, A Poem. Migration, A Poem. 16mo, roan back, marbled sides, cover loose, pp. 124, UNCUT EDGES.

Boston: Hilliard, Gray, Little, and Wilkins, 1827

This volume has become rare of late years. FINE COPY. Not in Sturges. Book-plate of Henry B. Anthony.

538. MICROCOSMUS PHILADELPHICUS: in Two Epistles to My Cousin Tom in New York. By Notus Nulli, Esq. M. R. I. A. and Other Poems. . . 12mo, boards, pp. 60, UNCUT EDGES.        Philadelphia: Printed for the Author, 1825

Delineates in verse the fashionable life and manners of members of the famous Philadelphia families, such as Biddle, Binney, Carey, Markoe, Ralston, Griffiths, Hazelhurst, Clapier, Ewing, Wilmer, Ritchie, etc., etc.

539. MIDNIGHT and Other Poems. 12mo, cloth, pp. 90—(lower corner water stained).        New York: For Sale by T. J. Crowen, 699 Broadway, 1858

Poems: "To the Poe;" "Columbia;" "To the Jews;" "Stewart Holland;" etc. Not in Sturges, McKee or Maier.

540. MILBURN (MRS. WILLIAM H.). Poems of Faith and Affection. 18mo, original cloth, pp. [9], 2 to 103.        New York: Hurd and Houghton, 1866

"Lines written at Baltimore on the defeat of Henry Clay;" "Ramblings at Saratoga;" etc. The authoress was the wife of Milburn the Blind Preacher, six times Chaplain of the United States House of Representatives. Also author of "Rifle, Axe and Saddle Bags;" "Pioneers and People of the Mississippi Valley;" etc. Not in Sturges, McKee, Harris or Maier.

541. MITCHELL (JAMES E.). The Story of Jack the Hermit of the White Mountains. *Illustration.* Oblong 18mo, original cloth, 27 unnumbered pages.

[Boston] 1891

PRIVATELY PRINTED. Not in Sturges, McKee or Maier.

542. MODERN BATTLE OF THE KEGS (THE). By the Poet Laureate of the Know Nothings. Proclamation.—"Whereas! for the ease of Creation."—Mayor Conrad. 16mo, boards, pp. 12 and half-title.

Philadelphia: G. Collins, No. 1. South Sixth Street, 1854

Poem on, "Lager Beer and Beer Kegs." VERY SCARCE. Not in Sturges, McKee or Maier. Contains the Henry B. Anthony bookplate.

543. MOORE (MRS. BLOOMFIELD). Gondaline's Lesson. The Warden's Tale. Stories for Children and Other Poems. 8vo, original cloth, pp. X, [3], 4 to 226, 4.
London: C. Kegan Paul & Co., 1 Paternoster Row, 1881
A scarce volume by this New Jersey Poet. Not in Sturges, McKee, Harris or Maier. Civil War Poems, Sonnets, etc.

544. MOORE (CLEMENT C.). A Visit from Saint Nicholas. *Illustrated from drawings by F. O. C. Darley.* 4to, pp. 8.
New York: James G. Gregory, 1862
Moore's celebrated poem, "'Twas the Night before Christmas." THE FIRST SEPARATE AND ILLUSTRATED EDITION IN BOOK FORM. Not in Sturges, Harris, McKee or Maier collections.

545. MOORE (JAMES, M. D.). The Shepard of the Wissahickon, and Other Poems. 18mo, original cloth, pp. 92.
Philadelphia, 1871
PRIVATELY PRINTED. Not in Sturges, Harris, McKee or Maier. Written in a dramatic tenor.

546. MOORE (THOMAS). Home Poems. Written at Leisure Moments. 32 mo, original cloth, pp. 64.
[Williamsburgh] 1875
VERY SCARCE, PRIVATELY PRINTED at Williamsburg, Long Island. On pp. 26–28 is "President's Proclamation, Aug. 7, 1863." The poem starts:—"Good Abraham Lincoln Who sits at the head," etc. Not in McKee, Harris or Maier. The author was a shoemaker.

547. MORRISON (JAMES M.). Clarsach Albin and Other Poems. By James M. Morrison, including his Correspondence with Clark, McCammon, and Douglas [in Verse]. *Frontispiece (Mezzotint).* 8vo, original printed wrappers, pp. 108, UNCUT.
Philadelphia: G.B.Zieber & Co., 1847
One of the rarest volumes of Scottish-American Verse. Dedicated to Col. Alexander, editor of the "Messenger." Some of the poems are entitled "To Col. Alexander." It contains some poems by Robert Clark and quite a few by Moses McCammon, from (the Wilds of) Spring Hill, near Moreland, Wayne County, Ohio. This volume is a correspondence in verse between the different authors mentioned. Not in Sturges, McKee or Maier.

548. [MORTON (EDWIN).] Verse. Occasional. 8vo, original cloth, 89 unnumbered pages.
Morges, Switzerland: Lavanchy, 1889
A RARE VOLUME OF PRIVATELY PRINTED American verse by a Harvard Graduate, Class '55. Includes "Class '55. Sophomore Song;" poem "Gerrit Smith;" etc. Not in Sturges, Harris, McKee, Maier, etc.

549. MURPHEY (CHARLES). A Journal of a Whaling Voyage on Board Ship Dauphin, of Nantucket, Composed by Charles Murphey, 3d. Mate, on the Voyage. 16mo, original printed wrappers, pp. 39 and 4 of Advertisements
Mattapoisett, Mass.: Published by the Atlantic Publishing Company, 1877
Rare poem, not in Sturges, McKee, Harris, New York Public Library, etc.

550. NICHOLS (MRS. LOUISA H.). Poems. 12mo, original cloth, pp. viii, [1], 2 to 110 and errata leaf.
New York: C. S. Francis and Company, 1857
Poems: "American Battle Song;" "Hymn, On the occasion of the First Celebration of Thanksgiving in Louisiana;" "To General Jackson, in Anticipation of his Visit to Louisiana In 1828;" "Requiem on the Death of Jackson;" "To My Country, during the Troubles in South Carolina;" "To My Sons on going to the Rescue of General Taylor;" etc. A scarce volume of Southern Verse. Not in Johnson, Manly, Sturges, McKee or Maier.

551. NISBET (RICHARD). The Source of Virtue; A Poem. Large 4to, original wrappers, pp. [5] and 2 to 18.
... Printed by Edward L. Low, Saint Christopher's, [West Indies]
Price-Half-A-Dollar [1790]
Preface dated from Neirs, 12th month, 1790. Quaker author, wrote a pamphlet on Slavery, printed in London, 1792. Note the Americanism of the "Price-Half-A-Dollar" instead of English Currency, the result of Yankee Trading to Saint Christopher and the West Indies for Rum, Molasses, Horses, etc. Autograph of Samuel Rodman, 1792 on title; rip on title, page repaired. Nice copy of an extremely rare poem not in Sturges, Harris, McKee, Maier, New York Library List, etc.

552. NORRIS (MRS. FRANCES B.). Reasons for Hating Strong Drink, and a Plea for Suffering (?) Humanity that the Plague may be stayed [Verse]. 16mo, original printed wrappers.          Boston, W. & E. Howe, . . . 1860
Scarce Temperance Poem. Not in Sturges, McKee, Harris, Maier, etc.

553. NORTH STAR (THE): The Poetry of Freedom by Her Friends. 16mo, pp. 118.
Philadelphia: Printed by Merrihew and Thompson . . . 1840
Fine copy. RARE. COVER LOOSE. Not in Sturges. Edited by John Greenleaf Whittier, who also contributed some poems, and preface.

554. [NORTON (SIDNEY S.).] The Raid of Blak-rivvah. By Essen. 8vo, original wrappers, title on front wrapper printed in gold, inside text printed within heavy red borders, pp. 16.          [New York, 187-]
A very scarce poem, not in Sturges, Harris, McKee, Maier, etc. PRIVATELY PRINTED.

555. NOYES (IDA E. S.). Occasional Verses. Toasts and Sentiments. Selected from the large number of such productions composed for her friends by Ida E. S. Noyes, and now published by her Husband, La Verne Noyes, and presented to those intimate friends who desire to preserve these expressions of her bouyant spirit, rare good fellowship and kindly interest. *Portrait*. 8vo, half calf, silk cloth sides, gilt top, 117 unnumbered pages.
[Chicago (?), 1913]
A SCARCE PRIVATELY PRINTED ITEM. Poem to "Our President" (Roosevelt) and many other poems of Peoples, Places, Events, D. A. R., etc. The University of Chicago received a gift of three hundred thousand dollars from the Authoress' husband as a memorial to his wife.

556. ODD-FELLOWS OFFERING (THE), for 1854. Contributed chiefly By Members of the Order. *With Elegant Illustrations*. Twelfth Volume. 8vo, original red emblematic gilt cloth, pp. 320.
New York: Edward Walker . . . MDCCCLIV (1854)
Not in Sturges, McKee, Harris or Maier.

557. O'DONNEL (KANE). The Song of Iron and The Song of Slaves; with Other Poems. 18mo, cloth, pp. 72.          Philadelphia: King & Baird, 1863
Not in Sturges, McKee, Maier, etc.

558. O'HAGAN (THOMAS). Songs of the Settlement. And Other Poems. 8vo, cloth, pp. 70.          Toronto: William Briggs, 1899
FIRST EDITION. Presentation copy *To Warren E. Mosher with the best wishes of Thomas O'Hagan*. Not in Sturges, McKee or Maier.

559. OLIVER (ISABELLA). Poems, on Various Subjects. By Isabella Oliver, of Cumberland County, Pennsylvania . . . 12mo, original calf, pp. 220.

Carlisle: From the Press of A. Loudon (Whitehall), 1805

Poems:—"On the Death of General Washington;" "Sacred to the memory of the Rev. Dr. Witherspoon, late President of New-Jersey College;" "In memory of—Rev. Dr. Nisbet, Principal of Dickinson College" [formerly of College of New Jersey]; "In Memory of the late Gen. Alexander Hamilton, who fell in a Duel with Aaron Burr;" etc. etc. With long lists of subscribers' names, Pennsylvania, New York, Fredericks-Town, Md.; and Princeton, New Jersey. Not in Sturges. FINE COPY.

560. O'MEARA (HENRY). Ballads of America and Other Poems. 8vo, cloth, pp. 146.

Boston: Damrell and Upham, 1891

Chapters of Revolutionary War Verse ("Boston Massacre 1770," "Sam Adams," etc.); Civil War Period ("Martyr Liberator" [Lincoln], "Gettysburg," etc.); Dramatic (Harry Murdoch, burned to death in Brooklyn Theatre Fire); etc. Not in Sturges, McKee or Maier.

561. ONE WEEK AT AMER, An American City of the Nineteenth Century. Small 8vo, original cloth, pp. 119.

Boston and Cambridge: James Munro and Company, MDCCCLVIII (1858)

The poet starts with Sunday—The Church; Monday—The State; Tuesday—Mercantile and Financial; Wednesday—The Press and Critics; Thursday—Different Grades of American Slavery; Friday—Professional; Saturday—Fashion; with reflections on, and reviews of the doings at "Amer" a typical American City of the Period. Not in Sturges, McKee or Maier.

562. PAINE (HARRIET E.). Bird Songs of New England. 8vo, original boards, pp. 28.

Boston: A. Williams & Co., 1882

Not in Sturges, Harris, McKee or Maier.

563. [PAINE (THOMAS).] The Pennsylvania Magazine: or, American Monthly Museum for March, 1776. Number III, Volume I. 2 plates. 8vo, original printed wrappers, UNCUT EDGES, pp. [4] and 109 to 152.

Philadelphia: Printed by R. Aitken the Publisher, opposite the London Coffee-House, Front-Street [1776]

Edited (and partly written) by Tom Paine. Aitken the printer is authority for the statement that he could not induce Paine to write an article, unless he supplied him with a glass of brandy beforehand. Enriched with 2 copperplate engravings: I. Plan of Salt Marsh; II. A Perspective View of the Salt Works in Salisbury, New England, this last a large folding plate.

Among the "Poetical Essays" we find: "To the Memory of Capt. Jacob Cheesman, of the New York Forces" (100-line poem); "A Rebus upon the name of a city, the solution of which is (for Mystical reasons) expected from the learned Fraternity of Freemasons"; etc., etc. Extremely rare. Single numbers in above condition, very seldom offered. Not in Sturges, etc.

564. [PAINE (THOMAS).] Pennsylvania Magazine or, American Monthly Museum for June 1776. . . . With an Accurate Map of North and South Carolina with Georgia. 8vo, sewed, pp. [4] and 253 to 296; UNCUT EDGES, some leaves water-stained.

Philadelphia: Printed by R. Aitken, the Publisher, opposite the London Coffee-House, Front Street [1776]

EXTREMELY RARE. A chance seldom being offered to secure even single numbers of this Magazine which expired with the next (July) number. This is Vol. II, No. 3, only 7 Numbers in all were issued of the 2 vols. Not in the De Renne Catalogue. The map is a folding one in perfect condition. Not in Sturges, etc.

Poetical Essays are: "Ode to the British Empire," an unusual poem of over 210 lines, stating America's troubles with England (Charter, Taxes, etc.) and advising. "Old, generous England: freedom calls—awake," and other verse.

565. PASTOR (THE): A Poem. 12mo, original wrappers, pp. [5], vi to xvi, [1] and 2 to 50.
New-York: Published by F. & R. Lockwood . . . Wm. Grattan, Printer, 1821
Not in Sturges, McKee, Harris, etc. With an interesting 8-page preface giving history of this poem and its author.

566. PATTERSON (A. W.). Onward: A Lay of The West. Small 4to, cloth, pp. 28.
New York and San Francisco, 1869
Bookplate of Henry B. Anthony, and blind stamp of Brown University on title. NICE COPY. CALIFORNIA COPYRIGHTED.

567. [PAYNE (JOHN HOWARD).] Memoirs of John Howard Payne, The American Roscius: with Criticisms on his Acting, in the various theatres of America, England and Ireland. Compiled from authentic documents. *Fine engraved portrait.* 8vo, full old calf, pp. [5] and 2 to 131.
London: Printed for John Miller . . . 1815
Payne himself gathered the material for the above work, simply putting it in the hands of the publisher to be printed. Contains poems to Payne.
Not in Sturges, McKee, Harris, or New York Public Library list.

568. PECK (JOHN). A Short Poem, containing a descant of the Universal Plan; also, the Prosperity and Death of the Rich Man spoken of in St. Luke's Gospel, Chap. XVI. Added "Universalism . . . A Sermon" by Lemuel Haynes. Fifth Edition. 12mo.
Philadelphia: Printed and Sold by H. Probasco . . 1841
Very scarce edition of this Vermont Poet's work. Not in Gilman's *Vermont Bibliography*, nor in Sturges, Harris, McKee, Maier or New York Public Library catalogues.

569. PECK (LUTHER W.). The Golden Age. 12mo, original cloth, pp. 208, gilt edges.
New York: E. Goodenough [1858]
Temperance poem in Dramatic form. Not in Roden, Sturges, McKee, Harris, Maier or New York Public Library.

570. [PERRY (JOHN).] The [Masonic] Emblem; A Gift for all Seasons, *with New and Elegant Illustrations.* 8vo, original black roan, gilt (worn), pp. 263.
New York: Leavitt & Allen, no date
Contains an account of MASONRY IN NEW YORK IN 1776, by John D. Hoyt.

571. PHELAN (GEORGE F.). Gleanings from our Own Fields. Being selections from Catholic American Poets. 12mo, original cloth, pp. 110.
New York: P. O'Shea, Agent, No. 45, Warren Street, 1881
VERY SCARCE. Poems by Acton, Burke, Donnelly, Maurice F. Egan, Ellen C. Howarth (of Newark, N. J.), John Locke, John Boyle O'Reilly, John B. Tabb, etc. Not in Sturges, Harris, McKee or Maier.

572. PIERSON (MRS. LYDIA JANE). The Forest Minstrel. Edited by Rev. B. S. Schenk. 8vo, original cloth, pp. 264.
Philadelphia: J. W. Moore, 1846
Poems: To the Memory of T. W. White, late Editor of the Southern Literary Messenger: "To Mrs. Sigourney, 1844;" "The Shipwreck;" "To the Hartford Columbian;" "Spirit of Poesy;" etc. A poet of Liberty, Tioga Co., Pa. Not in Sturges, McKee, Harris or Maier.

573. PIETAS ET GRATULATIO Collegii Cantabrigiensis apud Novanglos. 4to, half old black calf and marbled sides, pp. xiv, [3], 2 to 106.
Bostoni-Massachusettensium Typis J. Green & J. Russell. MDCCLXI (1761)

    The "Pietas et Gratulatio" of Harvard College, The "Swan Song" of Early New England literature, was of little earlier date than the "Stamp Act."
    The above work is also interesting as being the first and only book printed with the Greek Types, sent over from London and presented to Harvard College in 1718 by Thomas Hollis. They were destroyed by the fire that consumed Harvard College in 1764.

574. PINDAR (CHRISTOPHER LAOMEDON). Alleghania; or, Praises of American Heroes. 8vo, original cloth, pp. 148.
Philadelphia: J. B. Lippincott & Co., 1868

    Subjects treated are: Lexington, Concord, Bunker Hill, etc.; Declaration of Independence; Washington, Trenton, Princeton; Indian Council; Brant and Burgoyne; Battle of Oriskany; Death of Herkimer and Baum; Green Mountains; Bennington; Stark; Valley Forge; Massacre of Wyoming; Carolina; Capture of André; King's Mountain, Yorktown, etc. Not in Sturges, McKee, Harris or Maier.

575. PINE (M. S.). A Glory of Maryland. Poem. A tribute of love and gratitude to the most Reverend Leonard Neale, D. D., The Second Archbishop of Baltimore and Founder at Georgetown, D. C., of the Order of the Visitation in the United States of America. 1817–1917. *Portraits and views.* Square 8vo, cloth, pp. 88 and errata slip.
Philadelphia: Salesian Press. Don Bosco Institute, 1917

    Historical Maryland Poem.

576. PLUMBER (WILLIAM). Ruth; A Pastoral Poem of Bethlehem Ephratah. 12mo, original printed wrappers, pp. 37.
Boston: Ticknor, Reed and Fields, MDCCCLII (1852)

    PRESENTATION COPY. Not in Sturges, Harris, McKee, Maier, etc. A rare title by this author.

577. POE (EDGAR ALLAN). The Raven. With Biographical Sketch of the Author. *Illustrated.* 18mo, original printed wrappers in blue and gold, pp. 24, unnumbered, gilt edges.
New York: Published by W. Jennings Demorest, 838 Broadway, [186–?]

    Very fine little edition of "The Raven," illustrated very nicely. Not in Sturges, McKee, Harris, Maier, etc. Very scarce.

578. POE (EDGAR ALLAN). Memorial Fund Edition. Price 25 cents. Select Popular Poems of Edgar Allan Poe. Square 16mo, original printed wrappers, pp. 32, partly unopened.    New York: W. J. Middleton, Publisher, 1881

    Not in Sturges, McKee, Harris or Maier.

579. [POE (EDGAR ALLAN).] COATES (REYNELL—Editor). Leaflets of Memory. An Illuminated Annual for MDCCCL. Edited by Reynell Coates, M.D. *Engraved plates 4 of which are illuminated IN COLORS.* 8vo, full contemporary morocco, extra, gilt edges, pp. 312.
Philadelphia; Published by E. H. Butler & Co., 1850

    Not in Sturges, McKee, Harris or Maier.
    Contains: "Sonnet to My Mother," by Edgar Allan Poe. The plates are "beauties," by Sartain and the binding is a choice American example of the period.

580. [POE (EDGAR ALLAN).] The Book of Rubies: A Collection of the most notable Love-Poems in the English Language. 8vo, full morocco, gilt, pp. 384, gilt edges, marbled fly-leaves.

New York: Charles Scribner & Co., 1866

A fine specimen of American printing and binding of the period, title printed in red, text printed in red and black thro'out within a red border. Not in Sturges, McKee, Harris or Maier.

Contains poem by Poe, "To . . .," beginning: "I saw thee once—once only—years ago;" "The Fugitive of Love," by Epes Sargent, other poems by George Arnold Aldrich, Maria Brooks, Bryant, Burleigh, Henry Clapp, Philip Pendelton Cooke, Dawes, Anne P. Dinnies (of So. Car.); Drake, Emerson, Embury, Thos. Dunn English, Hayne, Halleck, etc. A fine representative group of American poets worthy of a place in this fine volume.

581. [POE (EDGAR ALLAN).] DOTEN (LIZZIE). Poems from The Inner Life. 8vo, original cloth, pp. XXVIII and 171, gilt edges.

Boston: William White and Company, "Banner of Light" Office, 1864

Contains 6 poems by "Poe's Spirit" sent to the World through Miss Doten a Spiritualist. Sprague, Burns and Shakespeare have also sent contributions through the authoress.

Poe's [so-called] poems are: "Rusurrexi;" "Prophecy of Vala;" "The Kingdom;" "Cradle or Coffin;" "Streets of Baltimore;" and "Farewell to Earth." Not in Sturges, McKee, Harris or Maier.

582. [POE (EDGAR ALLAN).] HOWS (JOHN W. S.). The Ladies Reader designed for the use of Ladies Schools and Family Reading Circles: comprising choice selections from standard authors in Prose and Poetry; . . . 8vo, original cloth, pp. 425, [6 of advts.].       Philadelphia: E. H. Butler & Co., 1860

Fine copy although edges of some pages at end are stained. Contains "The Bells" and "The Raven" by Poe.

583. [POE (EDGAR ALLAN).] LARKIN (MARTIN). The Rival Collection of Prose and Poetry, for the use of Schools, Colleges, and Public Readers. 8vo, cloth, pp. 504, marbled edges.       New York: Sheldon & Company, 1877

Fine copy. Contains, Poe's poem, "The Raven." Not in Sturges, McKee, Harris or Maier.

584. [POE (EDGAR ALLAN).] Pearls of Poetry. *Illustrated.* 4to, cloth, gilt edges, pp. 68.       Philadelphia: Charles J. Peterson, 1885

Contains: "Annabel Lee," by Poe; "Indian Names," by Sigourney; poems by Bryant, Percival, Lowell, Emerson, Pinckney, Whittier, Drake, Aldrich, P. Pendleton Cooke, T. B. Read, etc., etc. Fine copy, not in Sturges, McKee, Harris or Maier.

585. [POE (EDGAR ALLAN).] WILLIS (N. P.). The Opal: A Pure Gift for the Holy Days. Edited by N. P. Willis. *With nine illustrations by Chapman.* 8vo, cloth, pp. 264, gilt edges.   New York: John C. Riker, 15 Ann Street, 1844

Contains "Morning on the Wissahickon;" "A Morning at Rome," by Thomas Bailey Aldrich, etc.

### FIRST AMERICAN POET'S MAGAZINE

586. POET'S MAGAZINE (THE). A Repository of Original and Selected American Poetry . . . Vol. I—April—No. I. 8vo, original front wrapper, pp. 48. Albany: Published by E. G. Squire, 58 State-St. . . . J. Munsell, Printer,

[1842]

Not known to Tassin in his *The Magazine in America.* A note on wrapper states that ONLY 2 NUMBERS WERE EVER PUBLISHED. Poems by the most noted American Poets of the period, Bryant's "Antiquity of Freedom" and "Excelsior," by Longfellow begin the volume.

*[Continued*

The Editor states he wishes to make it a repository of whatever is beautiful or grand in thought or expression. . . to make it in short, a common page where the Poet and the Admirer of Poetry may find the highest and best productions of the American Muse.
Not in Sturges, Harris, McKee, Maier and other sources consulted.

587. POLLOCK (EDWARD). Oration delivered before the Society of California Pioneers, at their celebration of the Seventh Anniversary of the Admission of the State of California into the Union. Ode: By Edward Pollock. San Francisco, September 9th, 1857. 8vo, original printed wrappers, pp. [2] and 24.          San Francisco: Printed by Charles F. Robbins . . . 1857
Besides the "Ode," Pollock wrote another "Poem," which is included in this pamphlet. Not in Sturges, McKee, Harris or Maier.

588. POWER (THOMAS). Lafayette; A Poem. 8vo, cloth, pp. 28.
                    Boston: Russell, Odiorne, and Metcalf, 1834
Presentation copy to Mr. Gordon from the author. Not in Sturges, Harris, McKee or Maier collections.

589. PRESTON (MARGARET J.). Beechenbrook; A Rhyme of the War. 8vo, cloth, pp. 94.                    Baltimore: Kelly & Piet, 1866.
Dedication to "Every Southern Woman who has been Widowed by the War." FIRST EDITION. Poems: "Stonewall Jackson's Grave," "Dirge for Ashby," Poems on Virginia, etc.

590. PRESTON (MARGARET J.). Old Songs and New. 8vo, original cloth, pp. 312.
                    Philadelphia: J. B. Lippincott & Co., 1870
Presentation copy to Miss S. A. Brock from M. J. P[reston]. FIRST EDITION. FINE COPY. Not in Sturges, McKee, Harris or Maier.

591. [PRINCE (J. C.).] Happy New Year. Third Annual Address of the Letter Carriers of the City of New York. January 1, 1866. Original blue glazed wrappers, printed in gold on covers, blue ink inside.
New York: Printed for the New York Letter Carriers' Association, by
                    Raymond & Caulon, 88 Cedar St., 1866
Letter Carriers' Addresses in Verse ARE RARE. Not in Sturges, McKee, Maier, etc.

592. Ps AND Qs. *Woodcut.* 6 lines of verse. Second Edition. 18mo, wrappers, pp. VI and 200.          Hingham [Mass.]: C. & E. B. Gill, 1831
Interesting Tales and Verse: "Hot-Tongs Society," "An Angler's Adventures;" "The Mournful Death of a Cat," in variegated complets; "To a Mosquito," written during one of that insect's operations—which accounts for its irregularity; and other curious tales and verse. Not in Sturges, McKee or Maier.

593. RAY (LUZERNE). The Coming Age. A Poem pronounced before the Phi Beta Kappa Society of Yale College, August 18, 1847. Original printed wrappers, pp. 16.
          New Haven: Printed by B. L. Hamlen, Printer to Yale College, 1847
Not in Sturges, McKee or Maier collections.

594. READ (THOMAS BUCHANAN). The Cable, Laid by the "Agamemnon" and "Niagara." A small glazed-finished card, 18mo in size, containing a 20-line poem.                    [Philadelphia, 1857?]
An extremely rare FIRST EDITION. Not in Sturges, McKee, Harris, Maier, etc.

595. READ (THOMAS BUCHANAN). Lays and Ballads. 8vo, original boards, paper labels, pp. 140 and 2 advertisement leaves.

Philadelphia: George S. Appleton, 1849

FIRST EDITION and hard to obtain. Covers loose. Not in Sturges, McKee, Harris or Maier.

596. READ (THOMAS BUCHANAN). Sheridan's Ride from Winchester. Song and Chorus written by T. Buchanan Read composed by David A. Warden. Large 4to, wrappers, pp. 5.

Philadelphia: Published by the Composer David A. Warden. 311-German St. . . . 1865

Respectfully dedicated to the author of the poem. FIRST EDITION SET TO MUSIC. Extremely scarce. Not in Sturges, McKee, Harris, Maier, etc.

597. REBELLIAD (THE); or, Terrible Transactions at the Seat of the Muses; A Poem, in four Cantos, Auctore Enginae Societatis Poeta. Edited and patronized by the Pi Tau. Printed by Private Subscription. 16mo, original wrappers, pp. 77 and "Acteurs" leaf.

Cambridge: Welch, Bigelow, and Company: . . . 1863

The author wrote this poem in 1819 but it was not printed until 1842. The characters introduced are: President Kirkland, (nicknamed Lord Bibo), Dr. Popkin (Dr. Pop.), Henry Ware (Sikes), John Brazer (Touchy), Levi Hedge (Logic), John Farrar (Screwem), Andrews Norton (Gad Norton), Sidney Willard (Willard), Jared Sparks (Sharks), all were professors at the time.
PRIVATELY PRINTED. Not in Sturges, Harris, McKee, Maier or New York Public Library list.

598. REDDEN (LAURA C.). Idyls of Battle and Poems of the Rebellion. By Howard Glyndon (Laura C. Redden). 8vo, cloth, pp. VI, [1], 2 to 3, [2], 6 to 152. New-York: Published by Hurd and Houghton, 1864

Poems: "Fall of Lexington Missouri;" "Belle Missouri;" "Douglas;" "Battle of Gettysburg;" "Jefferson Davis;" "Kentucky Crittenden;" "President's [Lincoln] Proclamation;" etc. etc. This is the Subscriber's edition with 3-page list of names beginning with Hon. A. Lincoln, President U. S., Gen. Grant, etc. All men of the day, from New York to California. Not in Sturges, McKee or Maier.

599. REEKIE (CHARLES). Day Dreams. 8vo, cloth, pp. [9], 2 to 198.

New York: L. D. Robertson & Son, Printers and Publishers, 1895

Presentation copy to Mr. J. R. Henchy, with the compliments of the author May 28, 1896. Not known to Ross. Not in Sturgis, McKee or Maier. Scotch-American Poet.

## RARE POEM ON THE NEW JERSEY COAST

600. RHAPSODY, A Poem. 8vo, unbound, pp. 19.

New-York: Printed by Hodge, Allen, and Campbell. MDCCLXXXIX (1789)

THE EARLIEST POEM PRAISING THE BEAUTIES OF THE JERSEY COAST.
This poem is recommended by the author only to the perusal of those "who are finely sensible of the beauties of nature, who are pleased with something more than the music of poetry." The romantic spirit is evident throughout the descriptions of the New Jersey Coast and in the ironical allusions to the vices of City Life. An extremely rare poem not in McKee, Maier or New York Public Library catalogues.

601. RICE (GEORGE EDWARD). Nugamenta; A Book of Verses. 12mo, original cloth, pp. 146. Boston: J. E. Tilton and Company, 1860

FIRST EDITION. Rice was also a Dramatic Author. He was a Boston Lawyer, Graduate of Harvard. Not in Sturges, McKee or Maier.

602. RICHARDS (WILLIAM C.). Retrorsum: A Poem delivered before the Alumni of Madison University, at the Jubilee Festival, August 4, 1869. 16mo, original cloth, pp. 48.　　　　　　　　　　New York: Hurd and Houghton, 1869

　　FIRST EDITION. The author was a Baptist Preacher in Georgia, South Carolina, Providence, R. I., and Chicago. Not in Sturges, McKee or Maier.

603. [RIDDLE (A. G.).] The Hunter of the Shagreen. A descriptive Poem. 12mo, wrappers, pp. 94.　　　　　　　　　　　　　Cleveland, 1882

　　PRESENTATION COPY from the author, with AUTOGRAPH on title of Will M. Clemens, Aug. 30th, 1882. Editor of 200 copies. Not in Sturges, McKee, Harris or Maier.

604. RIDGELY (JAMES). The Odd-Fellows Offering for 1848. Edited by James L. Ridgely and Paschal Donaldson. Frontispiece. 8vo, original cloth, pp. 288, [4 of Advertisements], gilt edges.
　　　　　　　　　New York: Edward Walker, MDCCCXLVIII (1848)

　　Has a frontispiece View of Odd-Fellows Hall, New York. Lossing, Chas. F. Hoffman, Grace Greenwood (Sarah J. Lippincott) and others were contributors.

605. [ROBERTS (MAGGIE).] Shadows and Silver Sprays. By Eiggam Stiebor. 8vo, original cloth, pp. viii, [1], 2 to 123.
　　　　　　　　　　　New York: John F. Troun & Son, 1875

　　Poems on the Orange Riots in New York City (with notes); On the Ruins of Chicago; To the Gallant Ninth Regt.; The Assassination of the Prince of the Erie R. R.D. (Col. Fisk); "Wreck of the Pasino;" "Explosion of the Westfield" (on its way to Staten Island, N. Y.); "Alexis out on the Plains," Civil War Poems, etc. Not in Sturges, Harris, McKee or Maier.

606. ROCHE (JAMES JEFFREY). Songs and Satires. Illustrated. 12mo, original cloth, uncut edges, pp. 100 and [3]. Boston: Ticknor and Company, 1887

　　FIRST EDITION, PRESENTATION COPY To Col. John B. Batchelder with the respects of the Author. Boston, April 1892. Not in Sturges, McKee or Maier.

607. ROGERS (GEORGE). My Adopted Country: A Poem, in three Parts. Part I: Freedom's Bower. Part II: The Emigrant. Part III: Life in the West. 8vo, original cloth, pp. 74, [1].
　　　　　　　　　New York: J. C. Riker, 129 Fulton St., 1851

　　Not in Sturges, McKee or Maier.

608. [ROOSEVELT (S. WEIR).] Address and Poem [The Age of Prose] delivered before the Columbia College Alumni Association at Hope Chapel, October 31, 1855. 8vo, unbound, pp. 36.　　　New York: M. B. Wynkoop, 1856

　　FIRST POETICAL WORK of this author. Not in Sturges, Harris, McKee or Maier catalogues.

609. [ROOSEVELT (THEODORE).] Victory! Celebrated by thirty-eight American Poets. Brought together by William Stanley Braithwaite. With an introduction by Theodore Roosevelt. 8vo, original boards, pp. viii, 84.
　　　　　　　Boston: Small, Maynard & Company, Publishers [1919]

　　FIRST EDITION. Braithwaite is a Negro author of much ability.

610. SAINT AND SINNER (THE). A Tale, Not Stranger than True. Frontispiece. 8vo, original illuminated boards, pp. 63.
　　　　　　New York: Published by E. N. Grossman, No. 59 Ann-Street, 1854

　　A poem of Lust, Passion and Redemption. Poems of this type are not usually found among Old American Verse. Not in Sturges, McKee, Harris or Maier.

611. [SALTUS (FRANCIS).] Comic Opera Plot Sonnets by Cupid Jones. 16mo, original printed wrappers, pp. 48.      Published by Musical Courier . . . 1885
FIRST EDITION, very scarce. With a 3-page letter by Francis H. Saltus laid in relating to above author's works. Not in Sturges, McKee, Harris or Maier collections.

612. [SARGENT (EPES—Editor).] The Emerald. A Collection of Graphic and Entertaining Tales, Brilliant Poems and Essays, Gleaned chiefly from the fugitive literature of the Nineteenth Century. 8vo, original cloth, pp. vi, [1], 4 to 316.                              Boston, John L. Shorey, 1866
"Goody Gracious and the Forget-Me-Not," by John Neal; "Stanzas," by C. H. Townsend; "The Burial of the Dane," by H. H. Brownell. Not in Sturges, McKee, Harris or Maier.

613. [SARGENT (EPES—Editor).] The Sapphire. A Collection of Graphic and Entertaining Tales, Brilliant Poems and Essays. Gleaned chiefly from the fugitive literature of the Nineteenth Century. 8vo, original cloth, pp. 319, [2].
Boston: John L. Shorey, 1867
Not in Sturges, McKee, Harris or Maier. "Ode," by Henry Timrod; "The Main Truck, or, A Leap for Life," by Wm. Leggett; etc.

614. SARGENT (HENRY J.) Feathers from a Moulting Muse. Small 8vo, original cloth, pp. vii, [2] 2 to 270.
Boston: Crosby, Nichols, and Company, 1854
Jenny Lind's Greeting to America, etc. The author was known as, Residuary Legatee of the late "Walter Anonym." Not in Sturges, McKee or Maier.

615. SAUNDERS (JAMES M.). A Collection of Miscellaneous Pieces, in Prose and Verse. 18mo, cloth, pp. 144.
Philadelphia: J. Crissy, 4 Minor Street, 1834
Preface dated from Bristol College, Penna. Contains "Ode," sung at the Annual Exhibition of Phillips Exeter Academy, August 22, 1832; "What is Life;" etc. Not in Sturges, McKee or Maier.

616. SAX (JOHN G.). Poems. 8vo, boards, pp. 4, vii, [1], 2 to 130.
Boston: Ticknor, Reed and Fields, MDCCCL (1850)
FIRST EDITION. Autograph letter by author laid in regarding the "Diamond" edition of his poems.

617. SCHOTT (GUY BRYAN). Poem by G. B. Schott, and the Valedictory by Donald G. Mitchell, pronounced before the Senior Class of Yale College, July 7, 1841. Published by Request of the Class. 8vo, unbound, pp. 48.
New Haven: Printed by B. L. Hamlen, 1841
This is also the FIRST PUBLICATION of a work by "Ike Marvel," written when he was but 19 years of age, just graduating from Yale College. A four-page poem song, "Thoughts at Parting," by R. S. Willis, is at end.

618. SCHUYKILL (THE). A Centennial Poem by M. K. C. *Illustrations.* 8vo, original cloth, pp. 48.                              Philadelphia: Jno. A. Haddock, 1876
Historical notes at end. Not in Sturges, McKee, Harris or Maier.

619. SEARS (REUBEN). A Poem on the Mineral Waters of Ballston and Saratoga, with Notes illustrating the History of the Springs and Adjacent Country. 18mo, calf back, board sides, pp. 108.
Ballston Spa: Published by the Author, J. Comstock, Printer, 1819

[*Continued*

[No. 619. SEARS (REUBEN)—*Continued*]

> RARE. FIRST LOCAL HISTORY in verse and prose of Saratoga Springs. The poem is a recital of the depredations by Indians of the Five and Six Nations and includes an account of the fate of Jane McCrea who was murdered and mangled by the Indians in a most shocking manner. PRIVATELY PRINTED AND A SCARCE IMPRINT. Not in McKee or Maier sales.

620. SEARSON (JOHN). Art of Contentment; with several Entertaining Pieces of Poetry, descriptive of the Present Times in the U. States of America. By John Searson Formerly a Merchant of Philadelphia. 12mo, pp. 225 and [1].                 Baltimore: Printed for the Author, by W. Pechin [1798]

> The rarest of Searson's Poems. Not in Sturges, McKee, Harris or New York Public Library catalogues. Small piece out of one leaf of the prose section. Dedicated to George Washington.

621. SEARSON (JOHN). Mount Vernon, A Poem: Being the seat of his excellency George Washington, in the State of Virginia. Lieutenant-general and commander in chief of the land forces of the United States of America This rural, romantic and descriptive Poem of the seat of so great a character, it is hoped may please. *With a Copper-plate likeness of the General. It was taken from an actual view on the spot by the author 15th. May, 1799. Also a cursory view of George-town, City of Washington, and the Capitol.* 8vo, original calf, covers loose, small hole & stain on margin of portrait, pp. 83

> Philadelphia: Printed for the Author by Folwell [1799]

> Not in Sturges or McKee sales.

622. SEWARD (MISS ANNA). Elegy on Captain Cook, to which is added, An Ode to the Sun. The Fourth Edition, with additions. 4to, new cloth, pp. 25 and half-title.
> Lichfield: Printed and Sold by J. Jackson, and J. Dodsley, in Pall Mall, London. MDCCLXXXIV (1784)

> Autographed by the authoress at end, *Anna Seward.* Not in Sturges, McKee, Harris or Maier.

623. SEWARD (MISS ANNA). Louisa, A Poetical Novel, in Four Epistles. By Miss Seward. The Fifth Edition. 12mo, original sheep, pp. [7], 2 to 80, [4]. New-Haven. Printed and Sold by Abel Morse. MDCCLXXXIX (1789)

> This copy has the EXTRA 3-PAGE POEM, "Few Happy Matches." The last leaf is pasted down and contains Morse's Advts. The poem is a Poetical Correspondence from "Louisa" to "Emma," her friend in the East Indies.

624. SEWARD (MISS ANNA). Monody on Major André. By Miss Seward. Fourth American Edition. 16mo, unbound, pp. 22.
> Boston: Printed and Sold by W. Spotswood, and C. P. Wayne. 1798

> As the authoress was an intimate personal friend of André, this poem has a special value, not attached to the writing of other verse on André. Not in Sturges, McKee, Maier or New York Public Library catalogues.

625. SHAKERS. Some Lines in Verse about Shakers. Not published by authority of the Society so Called. [8 lines verse.] 8vo, original printed wrappers, pp. 56.
> New York: William Taylor & Co. No. 2, Astor House. 1846

> Contains: "Lines by Charlotte Cushman (noted actress, poetess, etc.). Suggested by a visit to the Shaker Settlement;" (with an) "Answer to same from the Russellville (Kentucky) Advertiser." Not in Sturges.

626. SHIPPEY (JOSIAH). Specimens; or Leisure Hours Poetically employed on Various Subjects. Moral, Political and Religious. With Notes Critical and Explanatory: Also, a brief History of the Life of the Author, from the year 1778 to the year 1841; to which is added a Synopsis of all the parts of Learning by Samuel Johnson, D. D. President of Kings now Columbia College, New York. 8vo, cloth, pp. 238.

New York. Printed by Joseph B. Allee. 104 Beekman-street. 1841

Shippey was quite a character, besides being a New Jersey Poet, born at Raritan Landing and a relative of the Shippey Family of Rhode Island. He was a clerk to Gov. Tompkins of N. Y., Deputy Clerk Court of Sessions, N. Y., then Tompkins, Vice-President of the U. S. and an old friend, secured him a position as Bookkeeper in the U. S. Bank, and so on. Poems: "Ode to Free Masonry;" "Bird's Eye View [in verse] of our late Naval Victories. 1814;" other patriotic verse and many poems of New York interest, etc.

627. SIGHTS AND NOTES: by A Looker on in Vienna. Dedicated to the Union Army. Seventh [of November] Edition. Copy Righted and Corrected. *Illustrated.* 8vo, sewed, pp. [16]. Washington, 1864

Anti-McClellan item. Caption title reads: "Past, Present, and Future." Little General. Illustrations. Enter "Little Mac." (his birth) "Organizer! to a Great Army near the Capital," "Before the Chicago Convention;" "Nomination of the Peace Party, Chicago;" Baltimore, May 17, 1864 Coercion;" "Submission, Chicago, Aug. 29, 1864," etc. The poem is at end. With this goes a rare quarto-size BROADSIDE, "How Columbia receives McClellan's Salutation from the Chicago Platform" with key to names of portraits below. Not in Sturges, etc.

628. SILL (EDWARD ROWLAND). Christmas in California. *With fine woodcut illustrations by Helen Hyde.* Tall narrow 8vo, original wrappers, pp. [25].

San Francisco, no date

FIRST SEPARATE EDITION of this poem. Not in Sturges, etc.

629. [SILL (EDWARD ROWLAND).] Oration, Poem, [Man the Spirit, by E. R. Sill] and Speeches delivered at the Second Annual Meeting of the Associated Alumni of the Pacific Coast, held at Oakland, California, June 6th, 1865. Published by the Association. 8vo, unbound, pp. 108.

San Francisco: Towne and Bacon, 1865

FIRST EDITION, the earliest in bookform of Sill's poems. Not in Sturges, McKee, Harris, Maier, etc.

630. SIMMONS (HON. J. F.) Rural Lyrics, Elegies, and Other Short Poems. 8vo, cloth, pp. 228. Philadelphia: J. B. Lippincott & Co., 1885

Henderson, Ky., author. The first poem is on "The Press," written and read before a Convention at Aberdeen of the Mississippi Press Association. Not in Sturges, McKee, Harris or Maier.

631. [SIMMS (WILLIAM GILMORE).] [Drayton's Oration at the] Celebration of the 55th. Anniversary of American Independence by the Union and States' Rights Party. July 4th. 1831. 8vo, sewed, uncut edges, pp. [1] and 42 to 104.

[Charlestown, So. Carolina] 1831

Wegelin in his *Simms Bibliography* notes this item but gives no collation or title. It contains the following poems: Our Union, A National Ode by W. Gilmore Simms written and delivered by Simms; also, An Original Ode and Second Original Ode. Simms' poem is on pages 74 to 79.

This copy evidently lacks title and begins with "To the People" page, and then on verso of same is numbered 42 on to 104 as above given. On account of its rarity it has been offered although lacking general title-page. Not in Sturges, etc., etc.

632. [SMITH (ROBERT HOBART).] Fugitive Pieces, Etc. 1872. 8vo, original cloth, pp. 24. [Germantown, Penn. (?)] 1872

> The author's father, of whom a sketch is given in the volume, was an intimate friend of Baron Steuben, with whom he carried on a correspondence. He served under Washington in New Jersey and under Arron Burr in the Long Island and White Plains Engagements, Battle of Monmouth, New Jersey, etc. Not in Sturges, McKee, Harris or Maier.

### RARE VOLUME BY A MASONIC AUTHOR

633. [SMITH (WILLIAM MOORE).] Poems on Several Occasions, written in Pennsylvania. "Nec Lusisse Pudet." *Engraved frontispiece.* 16mo, original tree calf, pp. 141, one blank, and [2].
> Philadelphia. Printed and Sold by Enoch Story, in Second, between Chestnut and Walnut-Streets MDCCLXXXVI (1786)

> FINE COPY with the curious frontispiece. Contains: "An Ode," Addressed to the Brethren of Lodge No. 2 who had assembled together, on the Commons below Philadelphia between Delaware and Schuylkill to spend St. John's day in festivity June 24, 1782; "Melancholy," a poem Sacred to the Memory of Col. John Laurens; "Elegy," on a young Gentleman who had formed an unfortunate attachment and who, in hopes of overcoming it, went a Volunteer on the "Indian Expedition," but was wounded by the Savages (supposed to have been written by himself); "An Ode to the River Lehigh;" etc., etc.

634. SNOW (GEORGE W.). The Martyrdom of Jacques De Molay, the Last Grand Master of the Antique Order of Knight Templars. A historical Poem. 8vo. cloth, pp. [99], [1]. No place or printer [1885]
> PRIVATELY PRINTED MASONIC POEM. Not in Sturges, McKee, Harris or Maier.

635. SORAN (CHARLES). The Patapsco and Other Poems. Third edition, with Additions. 8vo, original cloth, pp. 194.
> Baltimore: Printed by Sherwood & Co., 1858

> Well-known poet of Baltimore and Washington. Poems, "Address to Baltimore;" "Hurrah for the Printers;" "Address for the benefit of Mrs. Willis" (American Theatre 1835); etc. Not in Sturges, McKee or Maier.

636. SOUDER (MRS. EDMUND A.). Leaves from the Battle-field of Gettysburg. A series of Letters from a Field Hospital and National Poems. *Illustrations.* 8vo, cloth, pp. 144.
> Philadelphia: Caxton Press of C. Sherman Son & Co., 1864

> Poems: "Sympathy from Germany;" "Song for the Union;" "An Appeal to Arms;" "Crossing the Border;" "Our Flag on Round Top." Some of this author's poems were published in Ballad form during the War. Not in Sturges, McKee, Harris or Maier.

637. SPAULDING (MRS. ANNA MARIE). Poems. 16mo. original cloth, pp. 287.
> New York. James Miller . . . 1866

> "Star-Spangled Banner," parody of Francis Scott Keys' Poem. Pages 15 to 90 are Civil War and Patriotic Verse. Others are on Vineland, N. J.; Missouri; "The Golden Gate" (California); etc. Vineland, New Jersey and Pennsylvania author. Not in Sturges, McKee, Harris or Maier.

638. SPIRIT OF FANATICISM: A Poetical Rhapsody. 12mo, unbound, pp. 12.
> New York: Published at the "Beacon" Office, 94 Roosevelt-Street, 1842

> The author, after attending some of the celebrated revival meetings of the time, and believing them to be nothing more than the effects of animal excitement, now offers this poetical production to the public as an exposition of his views on the subject. Not in Sturges, Harris, McKee or Maier collections.

639. SPIRIT (THE) of the Public Journals; or, Beauties of the American Newspapers, for 1805. 8vo, old calf, pp. 300.

Baltimore: Printed by Geo. Dobbin & Murphy, No. 4, Baltimore-Street; 1806

A RARE COLLECTION of rather queer Prose and Verse, selected in large part from Mississippi, Tennessee, Kentucky, Louisiana, Ohio, Indiana and other Western and Southern Newspapers of which a list is given. Not in Sturges, McKee, Maier or New York Public Library catalogues.

640. SPOFFORD (HARRIET PRESCOTT). Poems. 12mo, original cloth. pp. vi, [1], 2 to 172.          Boston, Houghton, Mifflin, and Company, 1882

FIRST EDITION of this Maine Poet. Not in Sturges, McKee or Maier.

641. STEARNS (CHARLES). The Ladies' Philosophy of Love. A Poem In Four Cantos. Written in 1774. By Charles Stearns, A. B. Since Pastor of the Church and Preceptor of the Liberal School in Lincoln. Now first published —according to Act of Congress. Small 4to, full old mottled calf, pp. 76. Leominster, Mass.: Printed by John Prentiss & Co. For the Author, 1797

Written in 1774. Now FIRST (PRIVATELY) PRINTED. The author, a Harvard Graduate, wrote this poem when 22 years of age. "Canto IV" is especially interesting as treating on an early New England habit of Marriage by "Private Contract," with footnotes to same. Not in McKee or Maier.

## THE RAREST VOLUME OF "DOGGEREL" VERSE ISSUED IN CONNECTICUT

642. ST. JOHN (PETER). The Death of Abel. An Historical or rather Conjectural Poem; Relating many things which might probably take place both before and after that Barbarous Fratricide. By Peter St. John of Norwalk in Connecticut. 12mo, new cloth, pp. [7] and 14 to 186.

Danbury, (Conn.): Printed by Nathan Douglas, for the Author. M,DCC,XCIII (1793)

PRIVATELY PRINTED. A queer lot of subscribers each taking mostly from 6 to 12 copies, the "Betts" family holding the record, having taken 39 copies in all, the "St. John" family 30 copies, etc. The poem begins:

"Silence thou mute enchanteress adieu!
Henceforth no more employ have I for you."

It is difficult to get beyond this, the remainder of the poem generally following a similar style to the beginning—an almost interminable lot of "Doggerel" fully carrying out the author's words on the title; viz.: that the poem relates, etc. The poet certainly committed "Fratricide" on this "Brother of his Mind" when he wrote the above. Not in Sturges, McKee, Harris, Maier or New York Public Library.

643. STOKES (REV. E. H.). Starlets by the Sea. *Illustrations*. 8vo, cloth, pp. 96.
Ocean Grove, N. J., 1895

A scarce volume of Jersey Verse and imprint. Not in Sturges, McKee or Maier.

644. [STOCKTON (MRS. RICHARD).] SMITH (REV. SAMUEL S.). A Funeral Sermon on the Death of the Hon. Richard Stockton, Esq. Princeton, March 2, 1781. By the Rev. Samuel S. Smith, A.M., Professor of Divinity and Moral Philosophy, in the College of New Jersey. 8vo, sewed, pp. 48, uncut.

Trenton (N. J.): Printed and sold by Isaac Collins, MDCC.LXXXI [1781]

Contains 2 original poems by Mrs. Stockton on the death of her husband, 90 lines in all. The only form in which Mrs. Stockton's poems were printed. Not in Wegelin, Sturges, Harris, McKee, Maier or New York Public Library list. One leaf of the "Discourse" is imperfect, otherwise a NICE UNCUT COPY.

645. [STODDARD (W. O.).] The Royal Decrees of Scanderoon, dedicated by the author To the Sachems of Tammany, and to the other Grand Magnorums of Manhattan. *Illustrations.* 12mo, original cloth, pp. 45.

New-York: Russell's American Steam Printing House. . . . 1869

Anti-Tammany Hall and Graft poem. Not in Sturges, McKee, Maier or Harris.

646. STORY (WILLIAM W.). Ode on the Anniversary of the Fifth Half Century of the Landing of Gov. John Endicott. Delivered before the Essex Institute at Salem, Sept. 18, 1878. 4to, sewed, pp. 29.

Salem: Printed at the Salem Press, 1878

Not in Sturges, McKee, Harris or Maier collections.

647. [STOWE (HARRIET BEECHER).] Lays of Liberty; or, Verses for the Times. 16mo, original cloth, pp. 54.

Boston: Bela Marsh, No. 9 Franklin St., 1854

Pages 26 to 50 describe "Uncle Tom's Cabin" in the following poems: "Eva's Parting;" "Dead Eva;" "Death of St. Clare;" "Hopeless Bondage;" "The Purchase;" "The Consoler;" "Remembrance;" "Uncle Tom's Grave;" "Eliza's Flight;" "The Noble Hearted Child;" "First Day of Freedom;" "The Family Reunited." The volume begins with poem "The Indians of Nebraska." Not in Sturges, McKee or Maier.

648. [STOWE (HARRIET BEECHER).] Pictures and Stories from Uncle Tom's Cabin. *Illustrations.* 4to, original yellow printed wrappers, pp. 32.

Boston: Published by John P. Jewett, 1853

EXCESSIVELY RARE FIRST CHILDREN'S EDITION giving text of the story and illustrating same with poems and pictures. Poems are entitled: "Sale of Little Harry;" "Eliza Crossing the River;" "The Defence;" "Arrival in the Land of Freedom;" Tom and His Wife have heard that he is Sold;" "Eva putting a Wreath of Flowers Round Tom's Neck;" "Topsy at the Looking Glass;" and others. At end is, "Little Eva Song," by Whittier, set to music. Like all children's books this has become somewhat worn, but in the hands of a competent binder it would turn out fine. Not in McKee, Maier, Harris, etc.

649. STOWE (HARRIET BEECHER). Religious Poems. *Illustrations.* 12mo, original cloth, pp. iv, [1], 2 to 107.     Boston: Ticknor and Fields, 1867

FIRST EDITION AND FINE COPY. Not in Sturges.

650. [SWEET (J. P.).] "A Day on Coney Island," containing a description of that celebrated Watering Place; Its Geological formation and Social History; with a graphic description of its Magnificent surroundings, as viewed from the Great Iron Observatory. Containing, also, an account of the "Dream of A. T. Stewart," in which he endeavors to extend his financial operations to our Dreamy Satellite, also, his introduction to several "Distinguished Lunarians." This dream was never before published. The work concludes with a brief description of the Principal Hotels at Coney Island, and finally foreshadows the ultimate submersion of this Lovely Island beneath the Frozen Waters of the Ocean. In Heroic Verse by Tad. Square 16mo, original cloth, pp. 31 and [4].

New York: Printing House of H. T. Cornett, 8 Spruce Street [1880]

The entire work is in "Heroic Verse" as the author calls it. The title is a curiosity of American Verse—wherefore the cataloguer, for Bibliographical reasons, did "Heroic Work" by copying it.

Not in Sturges, Harris, McKee or Maier.

651. TABLET (THE). "My tables—meet it is I set it down"—Hamlet. 16mo, original printed cloth, pp. [7], 8 to 220 and errata slip pasted on back of inner cover.     New Haven: Published by A. H. Maltby, 1831

[ *Continued*

Dedicated to James A. Hillhouse, the well-known Connecticut Poet. Contains the "Social Man" by L. M. N., a Tale of the American Revolution; "To an American Eagle," poem; "An Elegy on the Death of a Cat killed by Corrosive Sublimate," by G. G. (Nice Tid Bit for the Cat Lover); "K. Ferguson," by H, narrative giving adventures of Ferguson against the Western Indians in Illinois, etc.; "The Poet's World," by J. G. Percival; etc.
Not in Sturges, McKee, Harris or Maier catalogues.

652. TAYLOR (BERT LESTON). A Line-o'-Verse or Two. 12mo, original stiff printed wrappers, pp. 125.           Chicago: Reilly & Britton Co., 1911

Scarce when found in good solid condition, the heavy wrapper binding generally being broken. FIRST EDITION. Not in Sturges.

653. TAYLOR (GEORGE LANSING). The Progress of Learning, A Poem, delivered at the Celebration of The Centennial of Columbia College, New York, April 13th, 1887. 12mo, original cloth, pp. 46.
New York: John B. Alden, 1887
Not in Sturges, McKee, Harris or Maier.

654. TELFER (WILLIAM DUFF). A Reminiscence [in verse] of the First Battle of Manassas: A Camp-Fire Story of the Seventy-First Regiment, N.G.S.N.Y. By William Duff Telfer, A volunteer in the Ranks of the Regiment during the period of the first term of its service in aid of the preservation of the National Integrity. [2 lines verse.] Small 4to, cloth, pp. [5] and 2 to 58.
Sold by John Lee, Strand, London, England, and published and sold by the Author, W. D. Telfer, Painter in Oil and Water Color, Sixth Ave. and Eighteenth St., Brooklyn . . . [1864]

Not in Sturges, Harris, McKee or Maier collections.

655. [THIERS (W. F. J.).] Jeanette; A Poem with three portraits (as Wife, Widow and Wanton). By Aesculapius Non Vinctus. 8vo, cloth, pp. 92 and [2].
New York, 1857

PRIVATELY PRINTED poem on a Providence, Rhode Island, girl who in her later years became a "Lady of Easy Virtue." An account of her "Amours" is given in the poem. Not in Sturges, Harris or Maier catalogues.

656. THOMAS (E.). The Young Lady's Piece-Book; or, a Selection of Elegant Pieces in Verse and Prose, from Various Authors, Designed for the Use of Schools, &c. *With 2 engraved plates.* 18mo, boards, roan back, pp. 162.
Philadelphia: Published by Elijah Thomas, 1828

Published by the author. Not in Harris, Sturges, McKee or Maier. Thomas was a well-known Philadelphia Quaker teacher of Penmanship.

657. [THOMPSON (M. M.).] Plu-Ri-Bus-Tah. A Song Thats-By-No-Author, A "Deed without a Name" Perpetuated by O. K. Philander Doesticks. P. B. *Illustrated.* 8vo, original cloth, pp. 264, [11].
New York: Livermore & Rudd, 1856

SCARCE FIRST EDITION. Not in Sturges, McKee, Harris or Maier.

658. THOMSON (CHARLES WEST). The Sylph and Other Poems. 18mo, original boards, uncut, pp. 110.
Philadelphia: Carey, Lea & Carey, Chestnut Street, 1828

Poems:—"On Visiting Cohoes Falls;" "On the death of Jefferson and Adams;" "To the Bank of the United States;" "The Land we Live In;" "The Rainy Day;" etc. SCARCE.

659. TILDEN (LOUISE W.). Karl and Gretchen's Christmas. Small 4to, pp. 63.
Cincinnati: Robert Clarke & Co., 1878
An interesting Christmas poem. Not in Sturges, McKee, Harris or Maier.

660. [TIMROD (HENRY).] A Little Book: [of Verse] to obtain means for Placing a
Memorial Stone upon the Grave of the Poet Henry Timrod. [By Prof.
Wm. J. Rivers.]
For Private Circulation. Published for the Committee by Walker, Evans,
& Cogswell, Printers. Charleston, S. C., no date
FOR PRIVATE CIRCULATION ONLY; this copy was presented to Judge A. J. Requies,
New York. The author was Prof. Wm. J. Rivers. Not in Sturges, McKee, Harris
or Maier.

661. TOKEN (THE). A Christmas and New Years Present. *12 engraved American
Views—etc.* 18mo, original gilt calf, pp. 368.
Published by Samuel G. Goodrich, Boston . . . MDCCCXXVIII (1828)
THE FIRST VOLUME of the Token published, edited by S. G. Goodrich. Contains
American Historical poems and fiction by the best authors of the period. A fine
specimen of Early American Calf binding decorated in gilt on all sides; little rubbed,
writing on title. Contains a "Daniel Boone Plate."
Not in Sturges, Harris, McKee or Maier.

662. TOWNLEY (D. O'C.). Alderman Rooney, at the Great Exhibition: Another
Epic By Himself. *Illustrations by Magrath.* 8vo, original yellow-glazed
wrappers, pp. 22.          New York: New York News Company, 1867
Poem on the adventures of an Irish couple at the Great Exhibition of the American Institute, 1867. Not in Sturges, McKee, Harris or Maier catalogues.

663. TOWNSEND (GEORGE ALFRED). Poems. 8vo, original cloth (binding is spotted,
inside clean), pp. 160.          Washington, D. C.: Rhodes and Ralph, 1870
FIRST EDITION. By "Gath." The author was a noted Journalist, and was the
War Correspondent of the New York Herald in 1862. Not in Sturges.

664. TREADWELL (Augustus). A Volume of Verse. *Portrait.* 8vo, cloth, pp. 255.
Brooklyn, N. Y.: Published by the Author [1906]
PRESENTATION COPY, *To Dr. E. A. Keehe, with compliments of the Author.* Oct.
*14, 1917.* Not in Sturges. Poems on the Civil War; "Abraham Lincoln, 1863;"
"Centennial Ode," Delivered at Jamaica (L. I.) Town Hall, July 4, 1876; etc.


A SCARCE VOLUME OF VERSE BY JUDGE ST. GEORGE TUCKER OF VIRGINIA

665. [TUCKER (ST. GEORGE).] The Probationary Odes of Jonathan Pindar, Esq.
A Cousin of Peter's, and Candidate for the Post of Poet Laureate to the
C. U. S. In two Parts. [2 lines of verse from Horace.] 12mo, contemporary
marbled boards, pp. 103.
Philadelphia: Printed for Benj. Franklin Bache, MDCCXVI (Copyright
Secured) (1796)
Political Verse. Judge Tucker, the author, was born in Bermuda, June 29, 1752,
O. S. Went to William and Mary College. In 1778 he married Mrs. Randolph, the
Mother of "John Randolph of Roanoke." He became Judge of the Court of Appeals,
Virginia, upon the death of Edmund Pendleton in 1803. He was a man of literary
taste and of thorough patriotism in the Revolutionary War. The first of these poems
were printed in Philip Freneau's Gazette in 1793. Not in McKee or Maier, the
Sturges copy was rebound.

666. TRI-DEAD (THE), A Tale, With other pieces in Verse. By a Mechanic. 12mo, original front wrapper, worn copy, pp. 31.

Salem. Printed for the Author, 1832

Not in Harris, McKee or Maier.

667. TUESDAY, JANUARY 1, The Carrier of the New-York Evening Post to his Patrons. (A poem printed in the New York Herald, Jan. 2, 1804.) Folio, 4pp. [New York. Printed & Published by Michael Burnham] 1804

Poem makes mention of Bonaparte, "Massa Jeff" [Jefferson], Clinton, Prebble, Great Hamilton, etc. Poem of about 150 lines. Not in Sturges, McKee, Harris, Maier, New York Public Library or Wegelin.

668. UNDERWOOD (T. H.). Our Flag. A Poem in four Cantos. 12mo, original printed wrappers, pp. 41.

New York: Carleton, Publisher, 413 Broadway, MDCCCLXII (1862)

Not in Sturges, McKee or Maier collections.

669. VANITY VERSES. "Begot of nothing but vain fantasy," Romeo and Juliet. 12mo, cloth, pp. [6], 5 to 79, [1].
Published for the Author. New York. F. B. Patterson, Publisher, 16 Cedar Street. 1876

Poems on the City of "Saint Augustine;" "Fisherman's Reason;" "The Hop" (dance); etc. Not in Sturges, Harris, McKee or Maier.

670. VICTOR (MRS. FRANCES FULLER). The New Penelope and Other Stories and Poems. 8vo, original cloth, pp. 349.
San Francisco: A. L. Bancroft & Company, Printers, 1877

Contains sketches of EARLY LIFE ON THE PACIFIC COAST as well as the Verse. Dedicated to the author's friends on the Pacific Coast but especially to those in Oregon. By the author of "Eleven Years in the Rocky Mountains," etc. Not in Sturges, Harris, McKee or Maier.

671. VINTON (FRANCIS L.). The Guardian, A Diversion. Tall 8vo, cloth, pp. 127, [1]. New York: Sutton, Bowne & Co., 23 Liberty Street, 1869

*Mr. Andrew Doyle with the sincere regards of the author,* written on dedication leaf. Not in Sturges, Harris, McKee or Maier.

672. WADDLE (I. H.). The Dartmoor Massacre, Transposed in Verse, from the New-York Commercial Advertiser, of the 6th. of June last and the Boston Papers, of the same month. Being the authentic and Particular Account of the tragic Massacre at Dartmoor Prison, in England, on the 6th. April last, in which sixty-seven American Sailors, prisoners there, fall the victims to the jailor's revenge for obtaining their due allowance of bread which had been withheld from them by the jailor's orders. Price 15 Cents. 8vo, sewed, pp. 8. Boston, Mass. 1815

PRIVATELY PRINTED. Not in Harris, McKee, Maier, New York Public Library List. This item was thought "worthy" of a separate reprint by the Magazine of History, Extra No. 15. The Dartmoor Massacre was one of the most scandalous acts committed by the British growing out of the War of 1812.

673. WALSH (MICHAEL). Sketches of the Speeches and Writings of Michael Walsh: including his Poems and Correspondence. Compiled by a Committee of the Spartan Association. *Engraved portrait.* 8vo, cloth, pp. 104.
New York: Thomas McSpedon, General Agent, 25 Pine Street. Up-Stairs, 1843

[*Continued*

With the rare full-length portrait by Gimber, showing "Mike Walsh" as an Orator One of the Queer Characters brought to light by "Tammany Hall," New York City. "Mike" was a cartman driving a noble mouse-colored horse, when not engaged in writing verse and making speeches before crowds of "Noble Workmen." Not in Sturges, etc.

674. [WARD (J. W. JR.).] Yang-Pih-We-Wing-Tzonga-Foh: or, Musings Over a Cup of Tea. 4to, wrapper, pp. LI.
New York: The "Evening Mail" Office . . . 1868

The wrapper-title is "Yang, &c," and is printed in type from one to three inches in height, the fly-leaves are genuine Chinese paper printed in red. The poem is dedicated to Anson Burlingame and is signed, "An American Chinaman." Not in Harris, McKee, Sturges or Maier.

675. WARE (MRS. KATHARINE AUGUSTA). Poser of the Passions: and Other Poems. 8vo, cloth, pp. vi, [1], 2 to 148.
London: William Pickering. MDCCCXLII (1842)

An extremely scarce volume of the more modern American Verse, comprising:— "Ode" written for and sung at the Celebration of American Independence in Boston, July 24, 1825, "Sunrise on Catskill Mountain;" "The Ship, Southerner;" "Valedictory Address, spoken at Columbia College;" etc. Not in Sturges, McKee, Harris or Maier.

676. WARING (CLARA INGERSOLL). Faun-Fa: A Story of the Catskill Mountains, in Four Parts. With local illustrations and notes. *Illustrations, text printed within red borders.* Small 4to, boards, pp. 147.
Detroit: Ostler Printing Company, 1889

This poem is based on Indian fact and tradition. Not in Sturges, McKee or Maier.

677. WASHIAD (THE) or Siege of Washington. An Epic Poem, in three cantos. By an Eminent Conservative. Canto First [ALL PRINTED]. No place, 1858

SCARCE PRIVATELY PRINTED POLITICAL POEM being scenes from the experience of an office-seeker, and containing some account of the conspiracy of the "Outsiders" to secure appointments to the U. S. Govt. Offices in the Custom House and Post Office at Newburyport, Mass. Not in Sturges, Harris, Maier, McKee, etc.

678. WEBB (CHARLES H.—"John Paul"). Sea-Weed and What We Seed. My Vacation at Long Branch and Saratoga. 8vo, original cloth, pp. 228.
New York: G. W. Carleton & Co. Publishers, MDCCCLXXVI (1876)

FIRST EDITION, VERY SCARCE. "Vacation Verses" at end. Not in Sturges, Harris, McKee or Maier.

679. WEEKS (DELLA JERMAN). Legends of the War. *With engraved portrait of the Authoress by Sartain.* 8vo, cloth, pp. 63.
Boston: Mudge and Son, Printers. MDCCCLXIII (1863)

AUTHOR'S EDITION. PRINTED FOR PRIVATE CIRCULATION. Not in Sturges, McKee, Harris or Maier.

680. [WELBY (MRS. AMELIA B.).] Poems by Amelia [Mrs. Welby of Kentucky]. A New Enlarged edition. *Illustrated with original designs by Robert W. Weir.* 8vo, original full blind stamped morocco, pp. 264, gilt edges.
New York: D. Appleton & Company; Philadelphia, Geo. S. Appleton,
MDCCCL (1850)

THE FINEST EDITION of this Kentucky Poet's work issued. Amelia B. Coffuck was born at St. Michaels, Md., Feb. 3, 1819. When a child she removed with her parents to Kentucky, and resided in Lexington and Louisville. In 1838 she married George B. Welby. She died in Louisville, Ky., May 3, 1852. Not in Sturges, McKee or Maier.

681. [WEIDEMEYER (JOHN WILLIAM).] Real and Ideal by John W. Montclair [*i.e.*, Weidemeyer]. 8vo, cloth, pp. 119.

Philadelphia: Frederick Leypoldt, 1865

PRESENTATION COPY to Dr. Farley. Dedicated to Longfellow. Poems on "Niagara;" "Ode to Poesy;" "Stars and Stripes;" "Age of Progress;" etc., etc. Not in Sturges, McKee or Maier.

682. WELLS (ANNA MARIA). Poems and Juvenile Sketches. 8vo, original cloth, pp. 104.　　　　　　　　　　　　Boston: Carter, Hendee, & Babcock, 1830

The authoress was a sister of Mrs. Frances S. Osgood, born in Gloucester, Mass., 1797; married Thomas Wells of the U. S. Revenue Service. Not in Sturges, McKee or Maier.

683. WHEATLEY (PHILLIS). Heaven the Residence of the Saints. A Sermon occasioned by the lamented Death of the Rev. George Whitefield, A.M. . . . delivered at the Thursday Lecture at Boston in America, October 11, 1770. By Ebenezer Pemberton, D.D., Pastor of a Church in Boston.
To which is added,
An Elegiac Poem on his Death,
By Phillis,
A Negro Girl of Seventeen Years of Age,
Belonging to Mr. J. Wheatley of Boston.
8vo, unbound, pp. 31 and [1].
Boston, Printed: London, Reprinted for E. and C. Dilly in the Poultry.
(etc.) M.DCC.LXXI (1771)

Not in Sturges, McKee or Maier. The authoress was a slave, became a prodigy of intellectual ability, writing before she was 17, letters and poems which attracted the attention of learned men of the period.

684. WHEATLEY (PHILLIS). Poems on various subjects, religious and moral. By Phillis Wheatley, Negro Servant to Mr. John Wheatley of Boston, in New England. *With fine copperplate portrait of the Authoress.* 12mo, calf, gilt edges, pp. 124, [4].　　　　　　　London: A. Bell, M.DCC.LXXIII (1773)

Now RARE. FIRST EDITION. Phillis Wheatley was a young negress. She was sold in the Slave market at Boston to Mrs. Wheatley. She was taught to read and write by one of this lady's daughters and became the pet of the family. Sixteen months after her arrival she had learned the English language. She was the first American female negro poet. The Romance of her life will always make this book a famous landmark in American negro literature.
On Verso of title is the book plate of Sir Walter Rawlinson, Knt. of Stow Hall in the County of Suffolk F. R. S. & F. S. A.
Poems: "To the University of Cambridge, in New England," (Harvard); "On Rev. George Whitefield;" "To a Lady on her remarkable preservation in a Hurricane in North Carolina;" "A Farewell to America;" etc.

685. WHEATLEY (PHILLIS). Poems on Various Subjects, Religious and Moral. By Phillis Wheatley, Negro Servant to Mr. John Wheatley, of Boston, in New-England. 16mo, original boards, leather backs, pp. viii and 9 to 89 and [3].
Albany: Re-printed from the London Edition, by Barber & Southwick, for Thomas Spencer, Bookseller, Market-Street, 1793

VERY RARE EDITION, not in Sturges, McKee or Maier. The Harris copy and the New York Public Library copy are evidently imperfect if the pagination given in their lists is correct. Heartman's *Bibliography of Phillis Wheatley* gives the same paging as above copy, which is correct.

686. WHEELER (AMOS) AND DRAKE (ORRISON). A Tragedy of the Androscoggin. On the death of Four People, who were Drowned in the Androscoggin River, April the 21st, 1803. By Amos Wheeler. Wild River Tragedy.

[*Continued*

Murder! Suicide!! Charles Freeman of Gilead, murdered himself and wife on the morning of June 11th, 1851. The cause was jealousy. 18mo, original printed wrappers, pp. 20.   Gorham, N. H.: Mountaineer Print, 1882

Not in Sturges, Harris, McKee, Maier or New York Public Library List. The first poem was written in 1803 and the second in 1857, and published to save these old time memories from oblivion.

687. WHITE (GEORGE). Home Ballads; Devotional, Sentimental, Humorous. 8vo, original cloth, pp. 134.   Chicago: Moses Warren, 103 State Street, 1878

Not in Sturges, Harris, McKee or Maier.

688. WHITE (GRACE HOFFMAN). Christus. A Story of Love. 8vo, boards, pp. [4], 1 to 64, [1].   New-York: Privately Printed MDCCCCIX (1909)

689. WHITMAN (SARAH HELEN). Poem [eulogizing Roger Williams] Recited before the Rhode-Island Historical Society, on the evening of January 13, 1847; previous to the delivery of Judge Durfee's Discourse. 8vo, wrappers, pp. 6.
Providence: Charles Burnett, Jr., 1847

This author's FIRST SEPARATE PRINTED WORK. Mrs. Whitman is a daughter of Nicholas Power, a direct descendant of a follower of Roger Williams. Not in Sturges, McKee, Harris or Maier.
Durfee's Discourse is also bound in with Mrs. Whitman's Poems.

690. [WHITNEY (A. D. T.).] Footsteps on the Seas. A Poem by A. D. T. W. 12mo, original cloth, pp. 50.
Boston: Crosby, Nichols, and Company, 1857

FIRST EDITION, the scarcest of Mrs. Whitney's books. A poem on the Atlantic Cable. Not in Sturges, McKee, Harris or Maier.

691. [WHITNEY (THOMAS R.).] Address [by Wm. W. Campbell] and Poem [by Thos. R. Whitney] delivered at the dedication of the Hall of Alpha Chapter of the Order of United Americans, April 1st, 1845. 8vo, unbound, pp. 24. New York: Published by Order of the Chapter, MDCCCXLV (1845)

By the author of the "Ambuscade." Whitney was a member of Congress, 1855–57; he died in 1858. Not in Sturges, Harris, McKee or Maier.

692. WIGGLESWORTH (MICHAEL). The Day of Doom; or, a Poetical Description of the Great and Last Judgement: With Other Poems . . . Memoir of the Author, Autobiography, and sketch of his Funeral Sermon by Rev. Cotton Mather. . . . 8vo, cloth, pp. 118 and [2].
From the Sixth Edition, 1715.  New York: American News Company, 1867

The Memoir is by John Ward Dean. This edition not in the Sturges, Harris, McKee and Maier catalogues.

693. [WILKINSON (WILLIAM CLEAVER).] Webster, An Ode. O nostrum et decus et columen! 1782–1852. 4to, cloth, pp. [5], 2 to 122.
New York: Charles Scribner's Sons, 1882

This poem was written to defend Webster from the slanders of Prof. Austin Phelps The notes are intensely interesting. Not in Sturges, McKee or Maier.

694. WILLIAMSON (GEORGE). Gleanings of Leisure Hours. *Portrait.* 8vo, cloth, pp. 301, [1].
Published by the International Publishing Co., Detroit, Michigan, 1894

Not in Ross' *Scottish Poets in America.* Not in Sturges, McKee or Maier.

695. WILLIS (N. PARKER). The Winter Wreath. *Engraved plates.* Tall 8vo, finely bound in full contemporary stamped morocco with diamond shaped inset in green leather on both sides containing title, pp. 224.

New York: Leavitt and Allen, 379 Broadway [184–]

A SCARCE TITLE BY WILLIS. Authors represented in this volume are Willis, Mrs. Osgood, Grace Greenwood, J. Fenimore Cooper, Bryant, Sigourney, Charles Dickens, etc. Not in Sturges, McKee, Harris or Maier.

696. [WILSON (ALEXANDER).] The Foresters: A Poem, descriptive of a Pedestrian Journey to The Falls of Niagara, in the Autumn of 1804. By the Author of American Ornithology. 16mo, boards, pp. 100.

Published by Samuel Tomlinson, Bucks County, Penna. Printed by John Boyle, Phila., 1853

An edition much scarcer than most of the earlier editions. Not in Sturges, Harris, McKee, Maier or New York Public Library catalogues.

697. WILSON (JOHN LYDE). Cupid and Psyche; A Mythological Tale, from the "Golden Ass" of Apuleius . . . together with The Life of Apuleius, and some Notice of the Style of the Author. *Engraved plate.* 8vo, full old black calf, pp. 88.

Charleston, S. C.: Printed by B. B. Hussey, 48 Broad-Street, 1842

Not in Sturges, McKee, Harris or Maier. Scarce item by this Southern author.

698. WINCHESTER (ELKANAN). "Heaven's Great Jubilee," poem on pp. 32, 33, 34 of Winchester's Discourses [The Face of Moses Unveiled by the Gospel; or Evangelical Truths, discovered in the Law in Four Discourses]. 8vo, unbound, pp. 54 and [2].

Philadelphia: Printed and Sold by Enoch Story, in Second, the corner of Walnut-street, 1787

The author was born in Brookline, Mass., Sept. 30, 1751; later resided in Charleston, South Carolina, 1774–1780. In 1780 he became Pastor of the First Baptist Church, Philadelphia, and in 1781 he there founded a Universalist Church; later went to England where his poem "Progress and Empire of Christ," 1793, was first printed; returned and died in Hartford, Conn., April 18, 1797. Not in Sturges, McKee, Harris, etc.

699. WISCONSIN AUTHOR. BOOTH (MARY H. C.). Wayside Blossoms among Flowers from German Gardens. Small 4to, red cloth, gilt edges, pp. vii, [2], 2 to 190 and printer's leaf.

Heidelberg, Germany; Bangel & Schmitt, Milwaukee, Wisconsin, S. C. West, 1864

RARE AND FINE COPY of a scarce volume of Wisconsin Verse. Printer: Victor Gross, Darmstadt, Germany. This ORIGINAL EDITION is lacking in Sturges, Harris, McKee, Maier, etc.

700. WISCONSIN AUTHOR. SOUBRON (WILLIAM OTTO). Soubron's Souvenir Poems. Dedicated to His Friends by the Author. [With same title in German.] 16mo, pp. [15] and 4 to 253, [1].

Milwaukee, Wis.: Buch-Druckerei des "Banner und Volksfreund," 1878

Very scarce volume of German-American Verse. 15 Indian poems: "Dakota;" "Minnehaha;" "Hahatonwa;" "Juniata;" etc.; "Niagara;" "The Mississippi and Missouri;" "Am Rio Grande;" etc. Not in McKee, Harris, Maier, etc.

701. WISCONSIN AUTHOR. WILCOX (ELLA WHEELER). Custer and Other Poems. *Portrait.* 8vo, original cloth, pp. 134.

Chicago: W. B. Conkey Company [1896]

FIRST EDITION, not in Sturges (?), McKee, or Maier.

702. WISCONSIN AUTHOR. WILCOX (ELLA WHEELER). Drops of Water: Poems. 12mo, original cloth, pp. 132 and [4].
New York: The National Temperance Society and Publication House,
No. 58 Reade Street, 1872

A very scarce volume by Ella Wheeler Wilcox. A worn copy with dedication leaf imperfect. Not in Sturges (?), McKee, Harris, or Maier. FIRST EDITION.

703. WISCONSIN AUTHOR. WILCOX (ELLA WHEELER). How Salvator Won and Other Recitations. *Portrait.* 8vo, cloth, pp. 160.
New York: Edgar S. Werner, 1891

FIRST EDITION and a scarce title by this author. Not in Sturges (?), McKee or Maier.

704. WOODWORTH (SAMUEL). Poetical Works . . . Edited by his Son. In two volumes. 18mo, original cloth, Vol. I: pp. 288; Vol. II: pp. 283, gilt edges.
New York: Charles Scribner, Grand Street, 1861

PRESENTATION AND CHOICE COPY of the FIRST COLLECTED EDITION in Scribner's Blue and Gold series. *To my friend and classmate Henry Martyn Clarke, Jr. Frederick A. Woodworth, March 16, 1898.*

## RARE WAR OF 1812 POEM BY A VERMONTER

705. WRIGHT (N. HILL). Monody, on the Death of Brigadier General Zebulon Montgomery Pike: and Other Poems, [one line of verse]. 8vo, original boards, pp. 79.        Middlebury, Vt.: Printed by Slade & Ferguson, 1814

Gen. Pike, Soldier and Traveller, was born Jan. 5, 1779, in Lamberton, New Jersey. He was a surveyor of Louisiana Territory in 1805. He discovered that lofty peak of the Rocky Mountains in Colorado now called "Pike's Peak," after its discoverer. Other poems in this volume are: "Lines on the Battle of the Enterprise and Boxer;" "Ode on the Capture of the British Frigate Java," (by the U. S. Constitution), etc. The author of the above volume of poems was a printer by trade. Not in Sturges, McKee, Harris or Maier.

706. [WYNKOOP (M. B.).] Song Leaves from the Book of Life and Nature. By An American. 12mo, original boards, pp. 113.
New-York: J. S. Redfield, Clinton Hall, 1852

The author was a New York Printer and Journalist. Not in Sturges, McKee or Maier.

707. YANKEE DOODLE. *Illustrated by F. O. C. Darley.* 4to, original printed wrappers, pp. 12.        New York: Trent, Filmer & Co., 37 Park Row, [186–?]

Very desirable edition of this ballad, much used during the American Revolution, and later. Not in Sturges, McKee, Maier, etc.

708. YOUTH'S POETICAL INSTRUCTOR (THE), Part II. A selection from Modern Poets, British and American. 18mo, original printed glazed wrappers, pp. 144.        Belfast: Printed by Alexander Mayne, 34, High-Street, 1851

An important collection of anti-Slavery verse, by Whittier, Longfellow, Bryant, Maria Lowell, W. L. Garrison, etc. Not in Sturges, McKee, Harris or Maier.